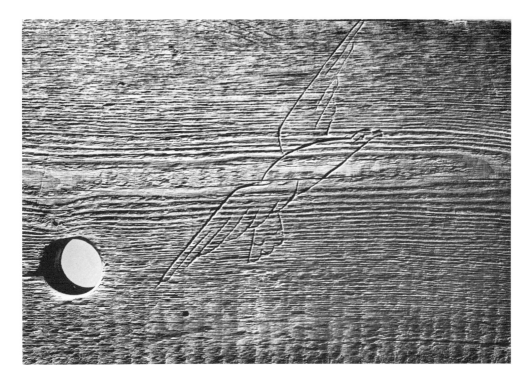

Taken from Bagley Bridge. Drawn in 1807 at time of building with a marking tool.

THE LAST OF THE
COVERED BRIDGE BUILDERS

By

MILTON S. GRATON
Ashland, New Hampshire

Clifford-Nicol, Inc.
Plymouth, N.H.

I

FOREWORD

Anyone who almost single handedly has repaired, rebuilt and even completely constructed twenty-two covered bridges deserves a marble pedestal in the antiquarian Hall of Fame. This has been the accomplishment of Milton Graton.

Sometime in 1931, nearly half a century ago by my reckoning, a likely-looking young fellow hit me up for a job hauling pulp wood. I was boss of the woods in those days. I liked the way the young immigrant from Winchendon, Mass. propositioned me. Not only did he want to work, but I soon found out he knew how. Soon he became a contractor, taking a few hundred cords of wood to haul, keeping every promise he made, which is what I expected.

What I didn't know was that Graton was a prospective master craftsman. In order to qualify, he became a New Hampshire Yankee who interested himself in such things as barns and bridges and other edifices peculiar to early rural New Hampshire.

After the great flood of 1927, and those of 1936 and 1938, there was plenty to tax the skill of the wooden bridge builder. Preservation of many of the old covered bridges intrigued Graton and set him to work figuring out how to restore an old truss or a pier. He learned how to line up stringers and fit braces and what trunnels were. Many of these structures built between 1830 and 1870 Graton found decayed and disjointed, sagging between the piers, the roof lines wavy and irregular. Two of the bridges he tackled he designed and built himself. With the help of his boys he rolled these structures into place with such precision that the complete bridge came to rest exactly as Graton had planned.

The most daring undertaking was the repair of the Bedell Bridge crossing the Connecticut at Newbury, Vermont. Saving this bridge from dropping into the river represented the culmination of all the acquired skills of the Graton family. Together with the delightfully executed bridge in Woodstock, Vermont, the bridges described in this volume round out a significant and colorful contribution to the preservation of the New England heritage.

Sherman Adams

Sherman Adams

Editor's Note: Sherman Adams was Governor of New Hampshire and a Presidential Advisor.

STATE OF NEW HAMPSHIRE
CONCORD 03301

MELDRIM THOMSON, JR.
GOVERNOR

The State of New Hampshire in recent years has witnessed a period of unprecedented growth and change. The increase in the State's population has brought profound alteration of the social and economic fabric which was primarily rural environment. This tradition is disappearing and as it departs it is sparking controversy among individuals, special groups and state government.

Along with the new and innovative land use programs for dealing with these existing problems the need for historic preservation takes its position beside New Hampshire's scenic beauty and its unspoiled environment. This book is primarily concerned with those needs, including perhaps foremost, the illnesses of our old historic covered bridges and the cures we have found over the last 20 years.

Sincerely,

Meldrim Thomson, Jr.

"LIVE FREE OR DIE"

Robert H. Whitaker
5 Rundlett Street
Concord, N. H. 03301

Milton Graton is almost unique to-day in that he
gets more store in the perfection of the products of
his brain and hand than he does in financial reward
for his efforts.

As a former State Highway Engineer and Commissioner
I have been familiar with a great deal of Milton Graton's
work in the field of wooden covered bridges.

Through the design, restoration and construction
of Numerous "Kissing Bridges" in New Hampshire and
elsewhere he has become the foremost living and
practicing authority on these amazingly durable
and romantic reminders of the earlier days of
our Country's transportation history. He executes
his work with complete authenticity down to
the most minute detail, with a degree of craftsmanship that is a joy to behold.

R.H.C.Whitaker

THE STATE OF NEW HAMPSHIRE
ROBERT H.
WHITAKER
No. 90
REGISTERED
PROFESSIONAL ENGINEER

NEW HAMPSHIRE DEPARTMENT of RESOURCES and ECONOMIC DEVELOPMENT

GEORGE GILMAN
COMMISSIONER

May 15, 1978

I have just learned of your recent publication covering restoration of covered bridges. I am delighted that you have put in print some of the techniques and procedures you have used in your outstanding career in this field.

Your work for the state on restoration of our covered bridges meets the highest standards of authenticity and craftsmanship.

I am looking forward to seeing the first edition of your book.

Thank you.

Sincerely,

George Gilman
Commissioner

RICHARD SANDERS ALLEN
RESEARCH CONSULTANT

13 ASPINWALL ROAD
ALBANY, N. Y. 12211 USA

May 23, 1978

In recent years, Milton S. Graton has become **the** man to see in regard to restoring an old covered bridge, or in building a new, authentic one.

Mr. Graton's livelihood comes from building covered bridges on the time-honored plans of more than a century ago, and in giving technical support, new life and dignity to old bridges which need to be adapted to the needs of modern traffic.

Covered bridges are not just "business" to Mr. Graton. He believes these structures are a part of our American heritage and should not be allowed to disappear, particularly as a result of neglect, apathy and an obsession for replacement. His convictions are admirably shown in his work.

Richard S. Allen

Editor's Note: Richard Allen is a Research Consultant from Albany, N.Y.

VI

PREFATORY

The first generation of Gratons arrived in this country with the British Army prior to 1725. After about 250 years in America, the Gratons are still a minority group; there being 60 family units according to 1960 U.S. Census. Every family tree bears some fruit: some drops or "drop-outs" and some specimens of mature fruit.

The Graton family, thus far, has produced one of the later each 100 years! Brig. General John Graton served in the Continental Army (U.S. Military Archives, Boston, "Field Officers of the Line"). Henry Clay Graton, founder of Graton and Knight Co. of Worcester, Massachusetts, the world's largest leather belt manufacturers, was publicly congratulated by President Hoover in 1931, at the age of 100, as the world's oldest living industrialist. He was also a director of Harvard University at this time. The mother of General Leonard Wood, one time Surgeon-General and Governor General of the Philippines, was of our family. The present I.P.C. of Bristol, New Hampshire was once a subsidiary of Graton and Knight Co.

Austin S. Graton
March 13, 1870 – Sept. 15, 1964

Catherine A. Graton
January 18, 1881 – May 9, 1925

The parents of the author who guided a large family with love and compassion and a very certain sprinkling of severity.

Daddy —

It was, and still is, a temptation for me to concentrate on one or two of my most vivid memories of my father as I was growing up, in order to indicate the breadth of his interests and the depth to which he pursued them. But, whatever my choices would be, the details of them would not be sufficiently developed here to give a complete picture of the man. I settled, instead, for a listing of some things which made a deep impression upon me and which, perhaps, went unnoticed for their significance by other people at the time.

His fascination with tools, wood, stone and cement bordered on rapture. That was translated, before he began to work on covered bridges, into building our home and those of others, of course, but, most exciting to me were the wooden mechanical toys which he built. And, he even interested a department store in selling them! They were original inventions and I can remember quite vividly the smell of banana-oil-based paint with which he added the finishing touches. I was even permitted to help dip some of the parts!

And building apple boxes or crates was another activity which allowed me an opportunity to work with Daddy. I could stack some of the slats as they were cut and unstack them as the men were ready to put the boxes together. His own design and assembly areas were both innovative and functional. And he taught me the smell of the different woods.

Daddy's unique approach to building a beach at the shore of Little Squam Lake, in front of our home, was to take wheelbarrow and truck loads of sand from my maternal grandmother's gravel pit behind our home. But, I thought it was quite interesting that he chose to do it in the winter and to place it on the ice just before the spring thaw. That allowed the sand to be placed further out into the lake, rather than just the few feet a shovel full could be tossed from the shore! It formed the start of a perfect permanent beach, which has only needed "topping-off" now and then with buckets of sand carried by us children when we went swimming and by Daddy's wheelbarrow when he went to the water.

And, speaking of water, even though the rule was always that there would be no swimming until my birthday each year — June 18 — because the ice had left the lake still too cold, I can remember many times when Daddy would get us up very early in the morning, have us put on our swimsuits, take a towel and go down to the lake. We would stand on a neighbor's dock and he would dip us off the edge into the lake, while he held onto our arms above our heads! Sometimes it was quite cold.

Ice-boating was fun, also. He built "sails" out of large pieces of cardboard, bordered with strips of wood. The "boats" were small snow-sleds. Picks for some control and assistance in "take-off" were filed off nails driven into sticks. With him on the "boat" with either one or two of us children, we would often "sail" across the cove or make our way out into the middle of the lake and **really** "sail" with the wind. After travelling about half a mile down the lake at about thirty miles an hour, we knew that we had travelled. Those were the days when the speed limit signs I can remember were never over twenty-five. To stop ourselves, we often had to simply all fall off the "boat" and try to catch the pieces — sail, sled, picks and each other, by trying to run in that wind!

The trailer he built out of plywood, Prest Wood and covered with leatherette was completely fitted, with a built-in washing machine, stove, refrigerator, shower and a table which folded out of the way, when the eating benches were then made into a double bed. The bunk beds were also built in. This was in 1937, I believe and it took us to Florida that year, I think it was that year, and to Florida again almost ten years later and to other places in between. This house trailer created quite a stir, then!

With all this, he was still basically an intellectual! He would deny it, though! The recitation of high school Latin, including the construction of puns from some of the lessons, fifteen and twenty years after completing the course, proved that he was wrong! It was great fun to listen to. His general wry, deep and fun humor was nice to be around.

And, while the country was deprived of a brilliant military engineer and officer, when Daddy was not able to attend Norwich University, Northfield, Vermont after being accepted, certainly historians' and preservationists' ranks have been immeasurably enhanced! He only mentioned that appointment to me on two brief occasions, but there was an obvious regret of the circumstance and condition.

There are literally thousands of things which come vividly to mind, often, concerning significant things which I remember about my early association with Milton S. Graton. I leave most of the "bridge building" telling to him, since I was already an adult living away from home when he began to concentrate on the bridges. I did, however, visit some of his bridges on several occasions, and gave a few slide shows and lectures on the history of such bridges and his work in particular. I am fascinated by it, certainly!

June E. Graton
Mrs. Robert Meitz

My Dad —

A real friend always ready to help anyone. I have enjoyed working with him and learning a respect for wood and wooden structures. For most of my life I have watched and helped with many of his unusual and difficult undertakings, including raising five children, which would have taken an ordinary man under.

Well, why don't you meet my dad in the next pages. I think you will find his writing much more interesting than mine.

Arnold M. Graton, Sr.

Daddy —

In many, many difficult situations in life, I've later had to thank God for the strength of character that Daddy built into me. I didn't always appreciate it at the time, for instance when I wanted very much to tell someone off, but something very deep inside me would not allow it.

I guess Daddy is building his bridges by a similar blueprint, thoroughly, correctly, with strength to last a lifetime.

Daddy is the only grandfather I know of who carries pictures of covered bridges instead of his grandchildren.

Isabel D. Graton
Mrs. Joseph Dittrich

My Dad —

For as long as I can remember, Dad has worked hard and of course he raised us that way too. I think he was reasonably successful in that endeavor and I don't feel he has been disappointed. Although we disagreed many times with what he wanted us to do, I feel we all are better people now because of his insistence on us doing it.

Although Dad didn't have as much time to spend with us as other parents may have, when he felt it was essential, he found the time. We did not have the opportunity to do some of the things that other children did because Dad was working so much of the time, but in a larger sense, we had many experiences and did many things that others did not. Many of these experiences are as a result of our spending most of our spare time working with him. By the time we were fourteen or fifteen, any of the three of us boys could do about anything in construction that Dad had taught us and do it nearly as well as any journeyman in that field.

Although we live many miles apart now, I feel we may be closer than we have ever been.

Dad's real love is construction and he has dedicated his life to it. Only in the last twenty years however, has he found his true purpose in life, the construction/restoration of authentic, wooden, covered bridges.

Major Austin S. Graton

My Father —

My Father has been a great influence on my life. His guiding hand through the years, has given me the ability to choose a way of life that is honest and hard working.

I know of not many men that at his age can still keep up the pace of seven days a week from dawn to dusk.

His love and ability with covered bridges will never be equalled.

Dad's engineering skills put a lot of so called "engineers", although college educated, to shame. When the "book" stops is when Dad begins to shine.

He is very seldom wrong in his decisions and I only wish I had his degree of resourcefullness.

I have seen Dad give away more in life than he has kept. One of his favorite expressions is "The Lord Shall Provide." Right again.

For one who writes very little I think I have, enough.

Stanley E. Graton

Milton Graton —

I first met Milton Graton nearly a quarter of a centruy ago and have been married to one of his daughters for more than twenty-two years. During those years, we have occupied different geographic locations so that our contacts have been limited to brief visits, short vacations and special events. As a consequence, I cannot offer the kind of close personal view that his children may provide. Because we share a common profession, that of engineering, I can provide some perspective on his achievements as a builder of bridges.

It has been my good fortune that some of the time we have passed in one another's company was spent on the deck of one covered bridge or another. A bridge is many things, but when it is shared with Milton Graton it becomes a classroom in engineering. How the load is shared by the bars of the truss, why the bottom chord is under tension, how to make a serviceable laminated arch and why joints should be tight rapidly become apparent. In the process, the pupil becomes aware of a profound respect for the achievements of the "old timers" who conceived the designs and then carried them out with such vigor and ingenuity. Although he never met them, those builders of the past centuries were the professors of my father-in-law's school of engineering. He learned the art and science of the covered bridge from the surviving examples of their work.

The process of rediscovering or reinventing a lost technique does not simply consist of executing faithful copies of the old works. It is rather an exercise in applied scientific research requiring careful observation, the framing of hypotheses, testing these hypotheses against the available facts and finally reducing the results of the scientific process to practice. This phase of his professional education took place during a number of repair and rebuilding projects sometimes undertaken without a real prospect of turning a profit. This may be viewed as the payment of tuition. The scientific process culminated in the two great original bridges in Woodstock, Vt. and Henniker, N.H.

One of the responsibilities of any professional is to record for those who will come later the body of knowledge to which he has contributed. The present book represents the fulfillment of this part of Milton Graton's professional responsibility. If you can't share a covered bridge with him, reading his book is the next best thing.

Lt. Col. Robert Meitz

Grandpa —

At the time of this writing, I have unfortunately not seen my grandfather, Milton Graton, for almost three years. My clearest memories of him are his smile, his gruff sense of humor, and his vast and apparent love for covered bridges: their building and restoration. As a future architect, a goal perhaps inspired by this admiration, I can feel a great sense of kinship with this love. Each bridge is like a child: newborn, needing to be coddled and shoved, persuaded to maturity, until the final moment when the oxen take the last turn and the bridge rests firmly on both buttresses. Injured, needing persuasion and love, existing old bridges often need almost complete replacement. The end result in either case is gratifying: a beautiful, useful, and durable addition not only to the transportation network and to the landscape, but also to our history and national heritage. My grandfather's work is the carrying-on of the traditions of generations of Americans. I am very grateful for the opportunities I have had to continue these traditions and look forward to the next opportunity.

Joanna L. Meitz

CONTENTS

CBS
NEWS

A Division of CBS Inc.
524 West 57 Street
New York, New York 10019
(212) 975-4321

By flood, and by neglect, America has lost half her covered bridges in the past 20 years. I am one of those who believes this is the kind of loss a great country can't afford; if we lose touch entirely with our past, we must resign ourselves to a bland and maybe even a bleak future. That is why I so much admire Milton Graton. I stood watching him restore the old Bedell Covered Bridge, which spans the Connecticut River between Vermont and New Hampshire, and asked him:

"Are you doing it the old-fashioned way?"

"Yes, yes," he said, "everything's done by hand power."

"Why do you do it that way?"

"To make it fit the structure. If you look at the workmanship, you don't have to be an ancestor-worshiper to admire the person who built it."

"Well-made, was it?"

"Oh, yes. Yes," Milton Graton said, "they were artists. These joints, look at them. You can't get joints like that made today. The workmen aren't here any more. They're all in the cemeteries."

Well, not quite all. In an age in which we do so many things fast, and wrong, Milton Graton still does things slowly, and right. He is the equal of the great craftsmen of our past, and, we may hope, a strong link in a chain of craftsmanship which will never quite die out in America.

There is an ancient injunction which Milton Graton lives by, whether he knows it or not. It is found in Proverbs, Chapter 22, Verse 28:

"Remove not the ancient landmark which thy fathers have set."

Cordially,

Charles Kuralt

June 2, 1978

Truss of Henniker Bridge.

INTRODUCTION

An account of the moving, repair, restoration and building of authentic covered bridges in New England and New York by those who did the actual work.

The Gratons, representing the present day appearance of a long line of carpenters and woodworkers, have engaged in the preservation of our invaluable Americana and, during recent years, especially the covered bridge. From designing through erection, this has been a concerted family effort.

We have always been interested in work in specialized fields, where the particular job seemed to be an orphan — one routine to no one. If there appeared to be qualified people interested in the job, then we would be wasting our time. The field would be well cared for. One has only a given amount of productive time and should not waste it if there is need for his skills elsewhere.

My father, who passed away in his 95th year as a result of a broken hip, was still mentally alert and aggressive. He was a very precise workman with no patience for the "good enough". We were always told, "Whatever you work at, try to be a perfectionist or leave it alone."

We have opened up the work of many of the masters of yesterday. Their faultless work has been examined very carefully in the process of making parts for replacement or members to splice where decayed.

Being the only ones in New England making a business of covered bridge restoration during the past fifteen years, it is felt that we have had closer contact with the past than many of our contemporaries. Should anyone in the future spend as much time at restoration, he must, of necessity, have lost contact by that additional length of time. Therefore, we have been asked by many covered bridge admirers to document the available knowledge before it is lost.

PURPOSE

It is not the purpose of this work to attempt to explain the layman's views on the American Covered Bridge or to point out the many designers and faultless builders whose skills may be imitated but will never again be equalled. This has been well and masterfully covered by others. It is my purpose to write an explanatory book, as one who has devoted the greater part of fifteen years to the restoration, repair, moving, and building of covered bridges; to detail some of the difficulties encountered, and to describe some of the methods employed in overcoming them.

Have you ever seen a covered bridge? I believe it is safe to assume that perhaps fewer than one out of five persons has seen one. Of those who have, perhaps very few have examined one thoroughly enough to reach a conclusion as to the function of each part. The equality of the wood and especially the exquisite workmanship would be still less in line for appreciation without a guide to point out the merits as seen by a critic.

This may appear immature and repetitious to the person who is very familiar with covered bridges. Let it be remembered that it is the person lacking fundamental knowledge and love for these landmarks in whom we are trying to instill an understanding that will help create a desire to preserve the irreplaceable.

Covered bridges, like houses, have certain components that are more or less common to all. The house has a roof, foundation, with few or several rooms depending on the size of family to be accommodated. The foundation may be of split stone or merely posts. The roof may be light for warm climates or framed strong enough to support the great weight of accumulated snows. So, too, is the bridge built with abutments of split granite or even on posts or piling. The roof may be steep and well braced for snows or may be nearly flat for warmer climates. It may be built wide for much traffic or narrow for a limited number of users. It may be framed fairly light for lighter loads and short spans, or very heavy for longer spans or heavier vehicles or loads.

However, unlike houses, there are perhaps no two covered bridges alike. The "project" house builder of today may create two houses very nearly alike. He is able to tailor the lots to fit the houses. If it were a rare case indeed of the same builder being retained to build two bridges on the same stream, he would have to accept the stream locations as the Lord has provided them. There would be little wisdom for him to do otherwise but to conform.

Of those who built well we have the one hundred-year old plus bridges as evidence. When a builder fell short in his judgment, the elements forced him to yield his location to the next builder. In many cases we find that he also overlooked the most common enemy, high water. Perhaps he thought that it could not happen again in the life span of his bridge.

That covered bridges were not spared on the countryside and were used wherever they could shorten the travel distance of the horse on dirt roads is very evident. On the first 9 miles of railroad track from Plymouth, N.H. to Woodsville the passenger could travel over, what is said to be, the longest straight track in New England and see but one railroad bridge. As he rode along this same track he could count five covered highway bridges.

Some time ago we were hired, as riggers and carpenters, to move the old Quincy Covered Bridge in Rumney, N.H. from the Baker River. It had stood twenty feet above the river's surface for about 100 years. It was to be moved one and a half miles and converted into a gift shop over another stream.

The condition of the bridge was not good. It had been neglected or abused. The covering boards had been stolen during the war years and the rain had beaten in across the entire width of the floor. The whole structure was a deep gray color.

As our time of starting the job of moving drew near, so did July 4th, 1954. On the night of July 3rd, the bridge mysteriously fell into the river and was completely destroyed.

The owner sold us the salvage for blocking (timbers of 4 foot lengths used by riggers). We expected we were buying only that which we wanted. Soon we learned that we had assumed the responsibility for removal of all debris which might float down the river and cause damage.

In taking the framed portions apart we noted that they were joined so accurately that in one hundred years the sunlight had not penetrated enough to discolor the surfaces at the joints.

I was convinced at that time that to preserve the work of these honest and true carpenters of one hundred years ago was the duty of every good citizen who would save for posterity that which can never again be reproduced. It is my firm belief that the person who **can**, but **will not bother** to do anything to preserve these priceless pieces of Americana is as guilty of their destruction as he who actually destroys.

BRIDGES

The Pont Fayette, named in honor of General Lafayette, crossed the Pemigewasset River below the confluence of the Baker and Pemi. Rivers in

Pont Fayette, Plymouth, N.H.

Plymouth. When this picture was taken in 1934, the bridge was being torn down to make room for a steel bridge. This is the southeast corner.

View of Pont Fayette from the Holderness Intervale. Bridge was set high enough to avoid flooding which often occurred in foreground.

Leaving Plymouth for the Holderness Circus Grounds

It is said that when a circus unloaded from the train and paraded in Main Street, they headed through the bridge for the circus grounds. However, when Jumbo the elephant reached the portal he tested the bridge floor and refused. He was taken back to the railroad yard.

XVIII

Holderness Bridge

When work on the new steel bridge was started in 1934, I unloaded a car load of their timber, blocking and machinery. I hauled this to the job site with my 2 ton truck.

The first car load of bridge steel soon arrived. The bridge company had paid me $2 per hour for myself and truck. That was big money, at least for me. Now they asked if I knew of anyone with a heavy rig who could be hired to haul the bridge steel to the job site. Some sections were 65' long and the ½ mile of street route had many sharp turns. It seemed that there was a good job to be had. The various components must be sorted out and delivered as needed in the bridge, so I asked for the job for myself.

They were not impressed by the size of my truck, but agreed that if I could find some men they would send over a foreman to boss them. I located two local boys.

I borrowed an old 2 horse bob sled, such as was used for the front end of loads of long logs in the woods and reported that we were ready. The foreman came to the freight yard and we attempted to load, but he had never had to work with such a rig before and soon became disagreeable. The local boys whom I had found became noisy and the 45 year old foreman left us. I thought that my good job was gone.

Soon the superintendent arrived and asked what I proposed to do. I told him that a foreman was not necessary if he wanted us to do the job.

We placed the front end on the truck body and the rear on the sled. There was plenty of hard, clean snow and the streets were not plowed very close. We had little trouble moving the entire bridge material to the job.

I had replaced their foreman, worked as a rigger and drove the truck which I furnished all for $2 per hour and felt very fortunate to have the job.

Looking south (Five Points)

One half mile north of Pont Fayette is a location popularly known as Five Points. This is the junction of 2 railroads, 2 rivers and one road.

The high water, shown in this 1927 photo, removed the covered Town lattice highway bridge and also the railroad bridge at right. A close examination will reveal the shining wheels of a coal car which was parked in the bridge to hold it down. A new steel highway bridge was built at a new location to the right of this picture and 2 years later made a part of a local grade crossing elimination project. The covered railroad bridge is on the Lincoln Line and was replaced with steel. It is from this point that the long straight line of track to Woodsville starts.

Smith Bridge

The next visible covered bridge on the Baker River would be Smith in Plymouth Township.

Quincy Covered Bridge, looking east

Perhaps a mile up river, when the farms and pastures were kept clear of brush, Rumney's Quincy Covered Bridge could be seen also on the left.

The Quincy Bridge was 125 feet long and of Long Truss design, resembling very closely in detail the construction of Smith Bridge in West Plymouth and the Blair in Campton.

Rumney Covered Bridge

Further west on the highway between Rumney and Rumney Depot is the Rumney Covered Bridge which was replaced in 1934.

Sandhill Bridge

This bridge, which for convenience we will identify as Sandhill Bridge for want of other identification, is in West Rumney on Sandhill Road. Since it was replaced in 1928, it must have gone out in the 1927 flood. No one was looking for a place to spend bridge money in 1928 if it could be avoided! We had this old picture and finally found a spot where it fitted the surrounding landscape perfectly. Fifty years had produced no noticable change.

STATE OF NEW HAMPSHIRE
By His Excellency
WALTER PETERSON, GOVERNOR

A PROCLAMATION

MILTON S. GRATON DAY

WHEREAS, Ashland, New Hampshire covered bridge builder,
rebuilder and preserver Milton S. Graton is recognized as a
craftsman without peer, and

WHEREAS, several organizations, namely, the Covered Bridge
Association of New Hampshire, the Connecticut River Covered Bridge
Society, and the National Society for the Preservation of Covered
Bridges, jointly are honoring the said Milton S. Graton at a testi-
monial June 7, and

WHEREAS, it is fitting and proper that we each show our
affection and esteem for the worthwhile things and institutions
of the past which we have inherited from those who lived in more
leisurely times and which are greatly deserving of preservation
in these tumultuous days,

NOW, THEREFORE, I, WALTER PETERSON, Governor of the State
of New Hampshire, urge all citizens and friends of New Hampshire,
with emphasis on those dedicated to the preservation of our own
three-score covered bridges, to join the Association and Societies
in tribute to Milton Graton and his associates on his appointed Day.

MILTON S. GRATON DAY

in our State.

Given at the Executive Chambers
in Concord this twenty-fifth day
of May in the year of Our Lord
one thousand nine hundred and
seventy, and of the Independence
of the United States of America,
the one hundred and ninety-fifth.

GOVERNOR

Walter Peterson

By His Excellency, The Governor

ATTEST: _Robert L. Stark_
                Secretary of State

THE COVERED BRIDGE ASSOCIATION OF NEW HAMPSHIRE;

THE CONNECTICUT RIVER VALLEY COVERED BRIDGE SOCIETY; AND

THE NATIONAL SOCIETY FOR THE PRESERVATION OF COVERED BRIDGES JOINTLY

PROCLAIM

MILTON GRATON DAY

IN

COVERED BRIDGE LAND EVERYWHERE

Whereas, the achievements of Milton S. Graton, of Ashland, New Hampshire, Covered Bridge Builder, Rebuilder, and Preserver, are worthy of special recognition.

Whereas, Covered Bridges are a priceless heritage and a part of our environment, worthy of preservation,

Therefore, the three Covered Bridge Societies of New England, listed below, do hereby join in declaring June 7, 1970, a day to honor Milton S. Graton, and we call on covered bridge people everywhere to observe this day in an appropriate manner,

Therefore, a program in honor of Milton S. Graton is planned on this date at the Sheraton Wayfarer in Bedford, New Hampshire,

Therefore, in recognition of the fact that Milton S. Graton has become a force for the promotion of the preservation of our Covered Bridges and our heritage, it is now hereby resolved that a LIFETIME MEMBER-SHIP in these three societies is granted to him, by

THE NATIONAL SOCIETY FOR THE PRESERVATION OF COVERED BRIDGES

THE CONNECTICUT RIVER VALLEY COVERED BRIDGE SOCIETY

THE COVERED BRIDGE ASSOCIATION OF NEW HAMPSHIRE

AND

COVERED BRIDGE ENTHUSIASTS EVERYWHERE

also expressing, in this way, gratitude and appreciation for the inestimable benefits which have occurred from a cordial relationship, together with the hope that the future may witness the same splendid co-operation.

Dated this SEVENTH day of June A.D., NINETEEN HUNDRED SEVENTY.

THE CONNECTICUT RIVER VALLEY COVERED BRIDGE SOCIETY	THE COVERED BRIDGE ASSOCIATION OF NEW HAMPSHIRE	THE NATIONAL SOCIETY FOR THE PRESERVATION OF COVERED BRIDGES, INCORPORATED

Tirzah P. Lincoln President	Richard E. Roy President	Richard P. Bonney President

NOTABLE AMERICANS
OF THE
BICENTENNIAL ERA

This is to Certify that

Milton Stanley Grāton

has been accepted to appear in the
1976 BICENTENNIAL EDITION
of
Notable Americans of the Bicentennial Era

Presented by the
AMERICAN BIOGRAPHICAL INSTITUTE
Subsidiary of HISTORICAL PRESERVATIONS OF AMERICA, INC.

J. T. Vickers
J. T. VICKERS
Editor

275 Mt. Vernon Avenue
Rochester, New York 14620
June 1, 1970

Dear Mr. Graton,

New York State Covered Bridge Society extends
congratulations to you on this special Milton Graton Day.

Please accept a lifetime Honorary Membership into
our Society, our recognition to you for the covered bridge
work that you do so well.

Most sincerely
and
Pleasant Covered Crossings,

Frances C. Withee

Frances C. Withee, President

New York State Covered Bridge Society

____Milton S. Graton____
is enrolled as a **Lifetime**
Honorary M E M B E R
of this society with dues paid from
Nov. 1, 19.......... to Nov. 1, 19..........

Richard Wilson
Treasurer

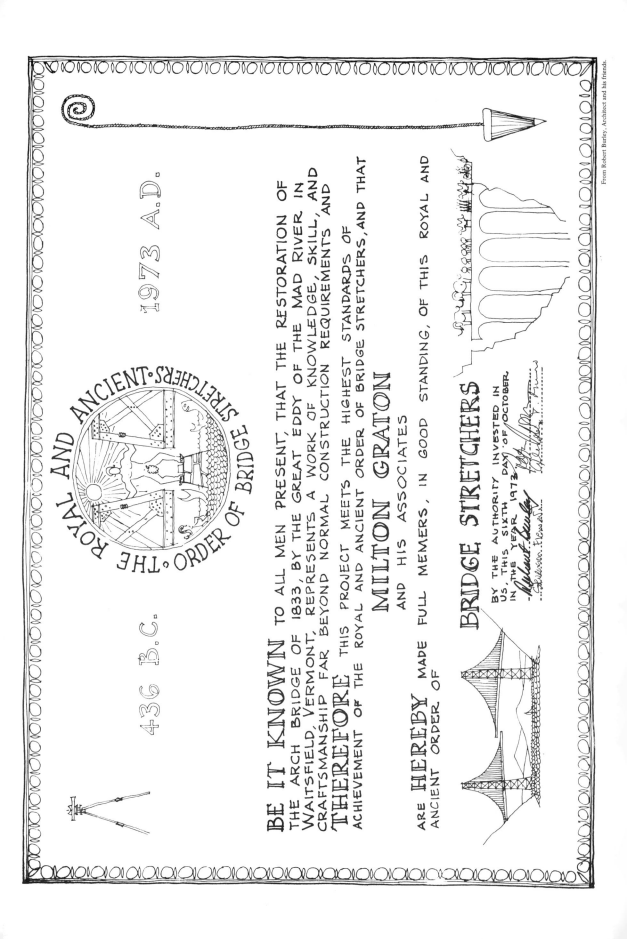

THE ROYAL AND ANCIENT · ORDER OF BRIDGE STRETCHERS

436 B.C.

1973 A.D.

BE IT KNOWN TO ALL MEN PRESENT, THAT THE RESTORATION OF THE ARCH BRIDGE OF 1833, BY THE GREAT EDDY OF THE MAD RIVER IN WAITSFIELD, VERMONT, REPRESENTS A WORK OF KNOWLEDGE, SKILL, AND CRAFTSMANSHIP FAR BEYOND NORMAL CONSTRUCTION REQUIREMENTS AND

THEREFORE THIS PROJECT MEETS THE HIGHEST STANDARDS OF ACHIEVEMENT OF THE ROYAL AND ANCIENT ORDER OF BRIDGE STRETCHERS, AND THAT

MILTON GRATON

AND HIS ASSOCIATES

ARE HEREBY MADE FULL MEMERS, IN GOOD STANDING, OF THIS ROYAL AND ANCIENT ORDER OF

BRIDGE STRETCHERS

BY THE AUTHORITY INVESTED IN US, THIS SIXTH DAY OF OCTOBER IN THE YEAR 1973

Milton S. Graton of Ashland, N.H., shown with Col. James F. Conti, U.S.A.F., President of Boston Post, Society of American Military Engineers, was guest speaker at the last luncheon of the season held recently at the Red Coach Grill, Boston. Now the only expert in New England making a business of building and restoring covered bridges, Graton's vivid description of his unique occupation, supplemented with 35 mm slides, captivated a large Boston Post membership, composed of top-flight engineers of greater Boston.

GENERAL

QUALITY OF TIMBER

Steel, unlike some other building materials, has certain basic characteristics. It can be tested and experimented with in the laboratory and certain qualities found that can be used to predict the behavior of the next bar or section of the same identical quality. Its tensile strength, its fatigue point, its crystallization resistance, can very well be anticipated from studies of identical material.

Granite and other stone of character differ in characteristics in the same close family. The laboratory and technician may develop certain basic values as crushing strength, but the many other qualities can only be judged by the man who has worked with stone and knows it thoroughly. He knows where he can pound all day with a heavy stone hammer, and do nothing, or where with short study he can peen a straight line along certain grain characteristics and open the stone in a straight line or even slice a stone as you would cake.

Timber, more than most materials, defies rules and tables. If nearly all the potential usefulness of a certain size timber is to be safely used, then one must know his wood thoroughly. If one has not the patience to study a piece of wood

1

and is unable to communicate with it, he may become its servant or victim rather than master.

The most common cause of timber failure, and more especially plank, is cross grain. Two pieces of plank for example may be placed side by side on a staging with identical span.

Two painters stand near the middle of the first plank. It could easily bend a foot and still hold the men safely. Now one man steps on the other plank at the same relative point that supported the two men. The plank breaks and lets the painter fall to the ground. There is at first no apparent reason, but an examination will show that the second plank, though as sound and firm as the first, was cross grained.

The plank, for strength, depends on the resistance to compression in the very top fibers and the resistance to tension at the bottom surface. Thus, when there ceases to be continuous fibers at the bottom, due to the fact that they reach the surface and end, the only fiber left is the softer layers between the yearly rings.

We all remember how hard it was as children to break wood for a camp fire, but how easily we could split it even with a small hatchet.

The first was an effort to break end grain or fiber.

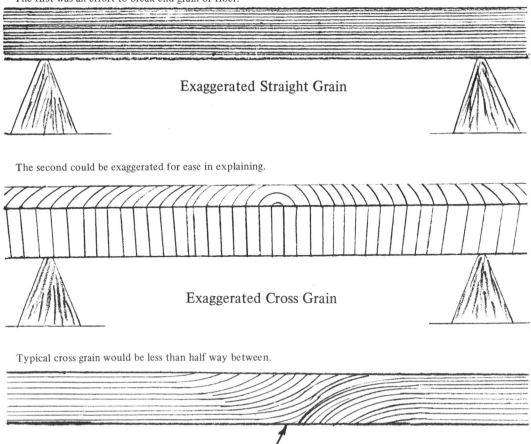

Exaggerated Straight Grain

The second could be exaggerated for ease in explaining.

Exaggerated Cross Grain

Typical cross grain would be less than half way between.

Typical Cross Grain

A plank with cross grain as below would be near worthless.

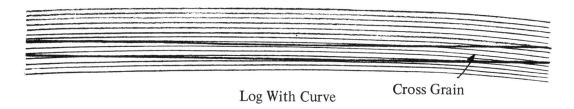

Log With Curve   Cross Grain

There are various causes for cross grain. The log or tree may have been crooked or the tree may have been twisted or "winding".

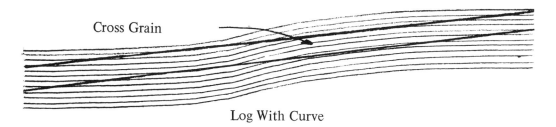

Cross Grain

Log With Curve

The first could produce a slash grain straight across the plank while the second could produce a slash in one direction to the center and in the other after passing the center.

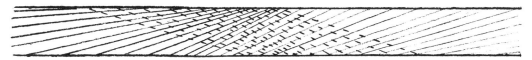

Dotted lines rep. grain on back edge.

Cross Grain Plank
Result Of Wind In Tree

Though the grain reverses at the center, the plank is nearly as weak as the first since each edge is without strength.

It is often thought that an old hewed pine timber becomes very hard with age. The truth is, however, that the hewed pine timber, if long at all, contained nothing but heart timber. This portion of the tree is mature and being of an old tree is very much unlike a young tree or the "sap" wood of an old one.

REASON FOR DURABILITY IN OLD PINE

Reason for durability — all sap wood gone. An 8" x 8" timber 40' long could have been 26" in diameter at the stump and all but 8" x 8" stayed in the woods as chips.

3

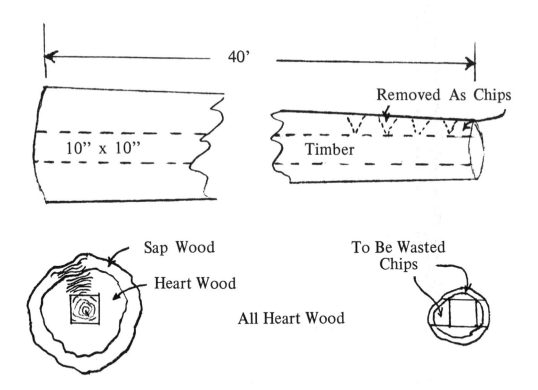

40'

10" x 10"

Removed As Chips

Timber

Sap Wood

Heart Wood

All Heart Wood

To Be Wasted
Chips

One 10" x 10" lower chord 55' long which we have seen in a Chelsea, Vt. bridge must have been three feet on the stump, and 4/5 was left as waste.

The good woodsman, after falling his tree where he wants it, (felling is the dictionary term when not in the woods) proceeds to cut off all limbs in such a manner as to leave nothing to project beyond the surface of the log or tree trunk.

He next sights the length of the tree to determine just where he should cut to avoid crooked logs. These make cross-grained, poor lumber, and in addition could, in square edge lumber, result in even less sawed lumber from a 16' long log than if it had been cut only 12' long. It is sometimes necessary to cut off some of the stump end of a log to raise the quality of the remaining portion. Also, there are times when a very crooked or faulty portion of a tree trunk is cut out and thrown away to raise the quality of the remainder.

The covered bridge in Chelsea, Vermont, while it is listed as being built as late as 1886, has hewed bottom chords. At that date it is believed the last of the up and down sawmills must have been gone — on a commercial sawing basis. The bridge lumber was sawed with a circular saw.

The reason for the use of hewed timber is very clear. Trees that would square 10" x 10" at 55' long had been found somewhere. Likely it was in a very inaccessible ravine where it was protected from wind and from the chopper during the "first cutting". Such a tree would have to be nearly 3' in diameter at the stump. There would be no sawmill that would have a carriage of sufficient length to saw such a log if it could be moved to the mill. The only sound decision was to hew it on the spot where it fell. This would eliminate 80% of the weight, and after some drying, still more.

In viewing his bridge, we can find other evidence of the perfectionist. Who else would go to such lengths to save having a splice in two timbers?

4

SOURCE OF MATERIALS

While working on the Flint Bridge in Tunbridge, Vermont, we found that the 80' bottom chords were made up of three timbers. The use of two members **might** have been better engineering, but there was, without a doubt, no sawmill that could handle 40' logs; at least within oxen-haul distance.

Since, of the six identical members in the bottom chords, two center members were hand hewed, and of the eight transverse timbers in the roof framing, four were hewed, it must be concluded that there was more than one source of timber.

The logical thought could be that there was a potential source of lumber or timber for the bridge, but "Farmer Brown" wished to pay his taxes in timber. He had plenty of trees nearby, had oxen to deliver the timber, but had no sawmill, so he was allowed to hew the timbers that he wished to furnish.

TODAY'S TIMBER VS. OLD TIMBER

The northern spruce of 100 years ago was or had been a very slow growing wood. All trees that would make the common chord size 3 x 12 32' long were 125 to 150 years old. They had grown in dense stands and though tall, the first 50 years would often make little more than a 6" tree. Either with the thinning by the first settlers in the back country or the acquiring of sufficient height to reach out for sunlight, the tree started to increase the size of its yearly growth rings for another 50 years, until it started its final years of nearing retirement. This period often counts 25 to 50 years.

The timber produced in this slow growing cycle is superb. It is quite free from the tendency to wind or twist. It frames nicely and is usually because of early "crowding", free from large knots. Of all framing timbers, it can be justly said, "This is the one".

Regardless of tables, laboratory tests, etc. this timber has the best weight-strength ratio of any timber I know. It may not be **supposed** to perform as it does, but if it moves out of character, we owe it still more credit.

The new timber of the same species will never reach the quality of its ancestor. It is thinned out, will grow faster, be of coarser grain, will not be as dense and strong, have larger knots, and our rapidly expanding need for lumber cannot allow time for the final slow growths of the mature years.

The greater crops that are being produced through selective breeding will indeed be a great help to the producer who is interested in square feet per acre only.

In the past, great stands of virgin spruce timber were cut into pulpwood. There was so much that no one could foresee the need to conserve. We find finish boards on old houses, even corner boards which get all the weather, that have served 100 to 150 years, and are still good. These were sawed from old growth pine heart. They may have been painted each 25 years with lead and oil.

Now compare this with the finish on the ranch house built 6 years ago. The paint won't stay on and the boards are already curling. This may not annoy many today, if they never used anything different. It reminds one of the younger fellow who can enjoy eating a piece of commercial apple pie simply because he has not eaten one made by Old Farmer Smith's wife.

It is not the intent to paint a morbid picture, but if the day of our best timber has not entirely passed, it is rapidly passing, and we should be conservation "worried".

ABUTMENTS

The abutment is a support on either shore of a stream, in our discussion. It is built of dry cut stone, usually, and is a well-laid wall parallel to the river with protecting wings. The wings are a continuation of the abutment face wall running at an angle back into the river bank. The purpose of the wings is to keep the water from washing behind the abutment wall. Behind the abutment wall there could be as much as ten feet of stone depth known as backers, which are packed or laid very closely. This mass of backing stone keeps the frost so far away from the abutment wall that any action of expanding soil, due to frost, cannot push the abutment wall into the river. Some of the split stone would weigh several tons and often reached a length of twelve feet. Granite being available in many places it became the stone commonly used in abutments.

Most of the covered bridge abutments outlasted the bridges. Many that have been out of use for years are still in perfect condition. They were built with the first layers of long split stone laid at right angles to the stream and projecting toward the stream to secure a balancing point for the abutment face. The walls were tied frequently into the backing stone with a long tie stone to make a secure wall.

Mortar was seldom used as the stones were fitted closely, showing excellent workmanship.

An abutment in Wentworth, N.H. which has not been in use for over 40 years, still in good condition.

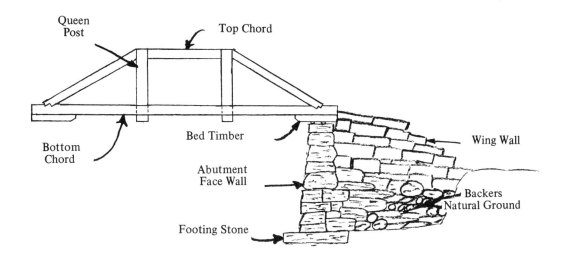

Queen Post

Top Chord

Bottom Chord

Bed Timber

Abutment Face Wall

Footing Stone

Wing Wall

Backers
Natural Ground

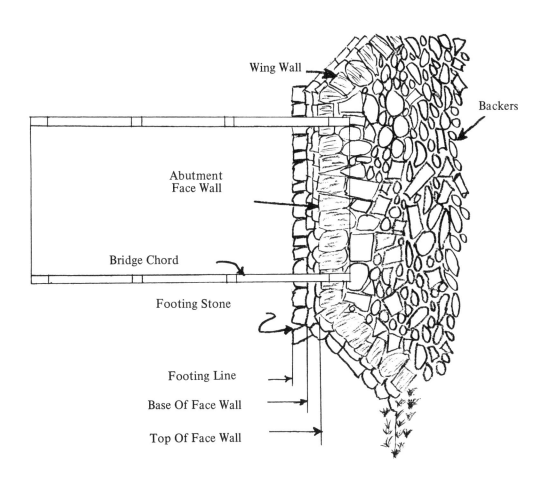

Wing Wall

Backers

Abutment Face Wall

Bridge Chord

Footing Stone

Footing Line

Base Of Face Wall

Top Of Face Wall

This abutment at the west end of Blair Bridge in Campton, N.H. was built in 1828. The many vertical cracks in the stones and rounded corners were caused by the intense heat when the previous bridge was burned in 1868. The abutment is built on ledge which is unusual.

MANY TYPES OF TRUSS

There are many types of truss and many modifications of any particular truss. Each builder had his own ideas as to how much timber surface exposure he should use to absorb the various thrusts in his own truss. Having rebuilt a bridge of one old master, one can readily recognize and identify in another bridge, of similar design, whether or not it is his.

Some used a double foot on their diagonal compression members, others used a square or more easily framed end. Some vertical members are simply framed through the bottom chord to absorb the horizontal thrust while others have also a shoulder cut into the top of the chord.

In most cases trunnels are used to fasten the various chord members together to form a continuous timber the length of the bridge. While shear blocks are more effective in developing greater holding effort in a shorter splice, they must depend upon bolts to hold them side by side. In repairing, we often employ the shear block for the above reason. In these splices we use dry oak, exposing the end grain to the thrust. We have been very fortunate in having access to the teachings of many of the old masters in opening up these structures for repairs.

Some points at which repairs more often become necessary, are as follows:
1. Bed timber on or near ground.
2. Bottom chord where it forms a container on bed timber and is not cleaned.
3. Bottom end of diagonal compression timber in framing. Accumulation of dust and dampness.
4. Road graded to allow water to enter bridge and washing of dirt around bed timber.
5. When laminated arches are employed, the settling of the bridge end places all the weight on the last supporting rods and arches become inverted.

AUTHENTIC WOODEN TRUSSES

There has been much controversy as to which type of truss is superior. Each that had a patent issued must have had at least apparent merits.

To me there are three basic types of truss that can be considered authentic, or made almost entirely from the forest. If we consider those employing functional iron rods, cast iron timber bases, and other metal accessories, we soon evolve into the TECO designs and to those employing little "framing" and relying on timber fasteners, bolts and gusset plates. Next we have the concrete slab with a cover and we have left the covered bridge entirely.

The covered bridge is loved and admired because of the fine and painstaking carpentry and framing that has gone into it, the imagination in wood, and the perfection that is seen throughout the structure.

There is the Queen Post which we find with many little sharp accessories. No two are nearly alike (save those built by the same master).

The Paddleford (representing the Burr family of trusses) is so much more sophisticated than the rest of the family that it could not grow on the drafting board nor could it be framed except by the imagination of the true genius. This type of truss is the best place for the expert framer to "show his wares".

The third, and the one where the greatest strength can be developed without the use of the arch, is the Town Lattice. This truss can be built in multiples of four feet or thereabouts.

It has been suggested that one reason for the popularity of the Town Lattice was that smaller timbers could be used. This is, however, in error. The lattice truss consumes more timber. The chords are pretty much the same in most bridges if the capacity and span were to be common to all. The vertical posts of the Paddleford on a long span would be 10" x 10" and in lengths of 16'. This would require a log 15" in diameter at 16' or the small end. Now the Town Lattice would require 4" x 12" in lengths of 20'. This would require a log 18" in diameter at 20' or the small end.

Now, if we were to cut the largest possible timber from each required log we would find the content of the "Paddleford" log 133 board feet and that of the "Town Lattice" log 12 x 12 – 20' to be 240 board feet. It is at once evident that the Town Lattice requires LARGER trees or logs.

BED TIMBER OR SHEAR BEAMS

These timbers are placed on the abutments at the four corners of the bridge and parallel to and directly under the bottom chords. Their purpose is to spread out the bearing weight. Thus this avoids having a concentrated pressure equal to ¼ the weight of bridge and load, against a small area of the bottom chord. The bed timber absorbs this punch and delivers it over an area perhaps twelve feet long. While any damaged part of the bottom chord would be difficult to replace, the bed timber is comparatively easy and requires little framing.

BOTTOM CHORD

The bottom chord consists of one or more timbers extending the full length of the bridge. It is a member common to all trusses. Though it may differ in make-up it serves a common function: to tie the bottom of the bridge together and resist the pushing forces from the top chord.

THE USEFULNESS OF ALL THE ROOF OR UPPER MEMBERS

You have doubtless looked into the top of your favorite covered bridge and wondered: "What are all of those timbers and braces for; and could the builder, with all his wisdom, possibly have imagined a use for them all? Did he put in braces until he could find no more places?" In years gone by some of these had been my thoughts. Since then I have found that every piece of wood has a function, and had been developed not on the drawing board but in the plain common sense department of the builder, after his communicating with his timber supply.

LATERAL BRACING

Some lateral bracing is needed in the top of all bridges. In the Queen Post it is mostly to resist wind in the roof and sides. Since the truss timber of the top chord is heavy and relatively stiff, the roof can be quite effectively braced with slanting braces from roof to posts in the side of the bridge.

In other types of truss where the span is longer, and the top chord is made up of many pieces, a well defined lateral bracing system is imperative. While some stiffness to resist sway may come from the floor, there must be no chance for the top chord to leave a straight line. Being under great compression there is a tendency to exaggerate any slight deformation that might develop. (See W-2 & W-2-A, under Woodstock, Vt. Bridge)

COVERED BRIDGE ILLS AND CAUSES

The covered bridge if cared for, even reasonably, could last for hundreds of years and especially with today's chemicals to prevent rot.

Except where side boards have been missing or rain has been allowed to enter through a leaky roof, a covered bridge never needs repairs other than ordinary wear in mid-stream. The damage occurs as a result of neglect. Dirt allowed to accumulate in vital joints attracts dampness and soon a settlement results.

Generally at this point, over the last 75 years, the local Road Agent came to the rescue. Often he was a hard working man with a good ability when it came to hauling gravel with his oxen or horses, but he didn't realize his bridge needed as expert attention as his road did. Consequently, the quality of the repair was very low and the bridge and its reputation for long life suffered. A major overhaul job would be in the making. From these observations, we must conclude the covered bridge has essentially only one enemy – neglect.

Recently, in rebuilding a bridge in Tunbridge, Vermont, it was found, upon removing the enclosing boards on the ends, that repairs had been made some twenty years earlier. At a point where the upper chord had been framed into the lower chord there had been a rotting condition. The bottom chord was cut off at a point where it is intended to take the total thrust of the top chord. A new shoulder was attached here with five 60 penny spikes. In repairing, this was removed with an ordinary 2' wrecking bar. The entire corner of this bridge, which had been carrying a Mack milk tanker truck as part of its daily assignment for twenty years, was being supported on a tiny secondary brace.

In the repairing or replacing of structural members of a covered bridge, it is necessary to place false work or cribbing in the river and jack the bridge in such a way as to relax all members. Thus when all repairs are made all parts go to work together.

If repairs are made while the bridge frame is under stress, the new member may look like a worker but will actually be nearly worthless for some time to come.

For the above reasons, it may cost as much to prepare to do a proper repair job, as it does actually to do the job.

METHODS OF RELIEVING INTERNAL STRESSES FOR REPAIRS

In the repairing of the covered bridge, we can liken the truss to the human spine. All other structural members are essential for the complete unit to function properly, but a failure here renders all other members useless. Therefore, when one looks for troubles in a covered bridge, his first area of concern is the truss and certain semi-working timbers upon which it must depend for support.

As mentioned before, any major stress member in a truss must be replaced while all other adjacent members are in a relaxed position. The replacement member is of necessity relaxed and no joint will become tightly intrenched in a working position without some movement. In an unrelaxed structure, the adjacent members are already in extreme stress as far as movement is concerned. For this reason there must be further failure in the structure before the new member can be of any service value.

The basic movement necessary in most structures to produce a relaxing is that which tends to produce or increase cambre evenly. This can be properly accomplished only by placing numerous jacking positions in the river bed and avoiding any undue concentration of pressure. It will, undoubtedly, become necessary to then jack from the floor to the top or various chords (depending on the type of truss).

In the Town Lattice type of truss, the trunnels will become more easily movable or in others the diagonal members will react to slight side pressure at the base. When this condition exists in an area adjacent to the member to be replaced, a reasonably accurate repair can be made.

SAWING UP A JOINT

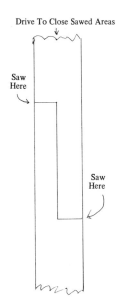

Drive To Close Sawed Areas

Saw Here

Saw Here

Sawing up a joint is the method used to produce an exact distance between two pieces of timber over the entire surfaces which are to be in contact. By sawing in the joint with a sharp hand saw the result will be a space, which we will assume, for our convenience to be 1/16" wide. We then close this gap by driving the timbers and yet maintaining the same alignment of the members. When the members are in contact the process is repeated if there appears to be any area that has not made contact.

This method of producing a 100% bearing is very satisfactory where two timbers have more than one common bearing area. As in a simple post splice, if both areas are sawed up each time before driving, the end joints should assume equal pressures if the same alignment is maintained.

12

SWEEP IN TIMBER

Perhaps sweep develops in at least 80% of sawed timbers. In some it is more pronounced than in others. It may become so great as to make the timber unusable in long lengths.

Usually this property is utilized in horizontal uses. If used as floor joists these timbers are placed with sweep or crown up. This tendency to rise in the center of the span will be countered by the intended loading and the end result may be a nearly straight timber.

Trees that have grown in a nearly perpendicular position and have not been crowded from one side, have not been forced to resist a prevalent wind, or have not found it necessary to grow all limbs on one side to get into an opening for sunlight, will generally saw timber that will remain straight and free from sweep. However, the above mentioned unfavorable factors produce internal stresses which counter them. When sawed straight, the timber which has been under stress and relieved, tends to "straighten" and thus produce sweep.

FRAMING TIMBER

Framing is the joining of two pieces of wood or timber into a workable combination by removal of parts of either or both pieces. It may involve the joining of two members to a complementary third member.

Skill in framing has been nearly lost as has the art of fine handwriting. Today, with modern equipment replacing human skills, the character that is said to have been read in the shaded handwriting of such men as John Hancock, is today sought for in the particular typewriter that he employs. The framing of timber is replaced by mechanical devices such as split ring fasteners. The man who replaces the framer needs no special skills. If he can drill a straight hole in the involved timber and use a simple wrench, he "has it made".

In the few places where a bolt is desirable, and has been used in the past, it is necessary to get the square nuts by special order. For convenience the industry has turned to hex nuts of automotive design. This nut has about ½ the bearing area of a comparable size in the square nut and beside being nearly worthless on today's thin washer, it looks ugly and out of place in a covered bridge.

SHARP LITTLE ACCESSORIES

Represented in Fig. 75 is a typical Paddleford post showing the shoulder which, by holding the bottom chord from falling, also supports the floor system.

The resistance to pressure from the forward diagonal member is in the area marked A-B & C-D. To produce the shoulder, it was necessary to reduce the end

13

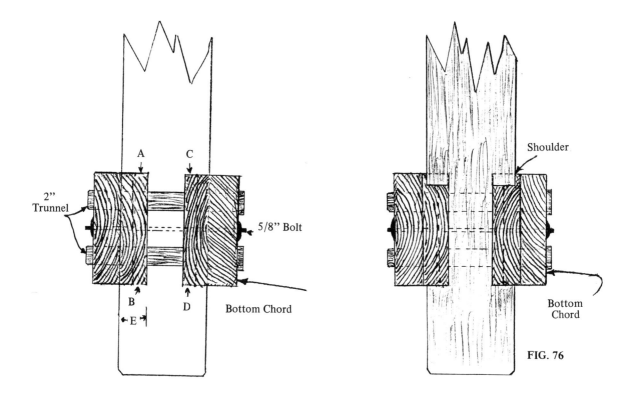

2" Trunnel

5/8" Bolt

A C

B D

E

Bottom Chord

Shoulder

Bottom Chord

FIG. 76

section of member E by one-half and consequently its tensile strength by that proportion.

In Fig. 76, the framing depths are decreased from the 1½" in Fig. 75 to 1¼. By losing less timber in the framing, it is possible to cut away for a 1" shoulder the entire width of the post framing. Though of small area, this shoulder is at a more serviceable height and prevents a tendency to split or be forced past the tennon portion. While this little example of fine and thoughtful framing has its merits, it provides one more spot for the gathering of dirt and dampness if there is the usual tendency to neglect.

It may be contradictory to most reasoning, but a covered bridge is stronger and more stable after a few years of service. This will allow for the grain compression necessary for a 100% bearing. Human error will not permit it to be achieved otherwise. However, grain compression corrects only slight variations and very close tolerance must be adhered to in framing.

We have seen many bridges carrying their normal loads, which, when disturbed for repairs, were found to have severe deterioration due to dirt and dampness.

In some instances, when framing was opened, the bond between the rotted portions of timber was greater than the tensile strength of the adjacent wood. The cleavage lines would indicate a deterioration so complete that there no longer existed in the wood a respect for parenthood.

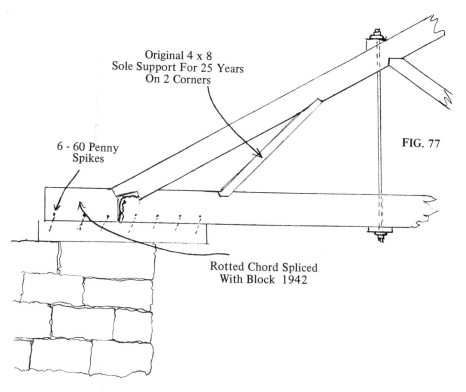

Original 4 x 8
Sole Support For 25 Years
On 2 Corners

6 - 60 Penny
Spikes

FIG. 77

Rotted Chord Spliced
With Block 1942

In rebuilding the Flint Covered Bridge in Tunbridge, Vermont we uncovered a little bracing arrangement that we have not seen elsewhere. It was not an "after thought" and after a useless repair, around 1942, on a complete end, the bridge could not have stood without it.

This is a typical corner repair at the Flint Bridge. By cutting away a sizable section of 10 x 10 bottom chord and replacing it with 10 x 12 we gained 2" of elevation and could spare 6" of bad timber at the end of the top chord, thus avoiding the waste of the entire old timber.

This new chord section and the old were then bolted to a 20' piece of 12" x 16" timber and made secure by a series of 2" trunnels to resist the end thrust of the top chord. The little underbrace was being installed.

PREPARING A BRIDGE TO MOVE

While the lattice bridge is extremely vulnerable if the proper precautions are not taken in jacking or supporting, there are a wide range of positions that can be used if spacers are placed between the chords directly above.

The weight of the bridge normally rests on the ends of the lattice. They meet, flush with the bottom chord, where they present a large bearing area in common with the chord members. If the jacking were done on the bottom chord, a concentration of weight would be brought on three or four trunnels whereas with properly fitted spacers, the stress would be distributed to the twelve or sixteen trunnels immediately above.

The Paddleford Truss on the other hand can be safely supported from the ends of two of the vertical members on any one corner.

To avoid a considerable amount of preparatory work, the Queen Post Bridge should be carried on that bearing area which is intended for permanent support.

STRENGTHENING OF RAILROAD BRIDGES

In the summer of 1967, Governor Hoff's office suggested to the Lamoile County Development Council and the Vermont Board of Historic Sites that we be invited to inspect three railroad covered bridges.

We were advised that the St. Johnsbury-Lamoile County Railroad was considering the destruction of three bridges. Heavier grain cars were now being used and were considered too heavy for the sixty year old covered bridges. To remedy this situation, the railroad proposed to drive piling bents and use shorter girder spans to replace the wooden bridges.

Since there are but a few active railroad covered bridges left in the United States, it was hoped that a method of strengthening these bridges with wood could be devised. Plans for the necessary strengthening were made which would not impair the original beauty.

Negotiations with the railroad were proceeding nicely when the inevitable happened. There was a confrontation with a high railroad official who was totally lacking in covered bridge sentiment.

It is said that he suggested the railroad stand aside temporarily. If others were willing to reinforce the bridges at their own expense, meet the railroad time table for completion and maintain the bridges afterward, permission to do so would be considered. Otherwise the railroad would go ahead with their plan to use steel.

This was so unreasonable that the plan was abandoned. However, it is understood that by contributing $14,000.00 to the East Walcott covered bridge expense, the bridge was allowed to stand though not bearing any traffic burden. This amount was raised through various organizations interested in preserving the railroad covered bridges.

TURKEY JIM BRIDGE

ORIGINALLY BUILT IN 1883

It is said that in the early 1880's the Branch Brook, during a freshet, changed its course. It actually split, creating an island of some 75 acres and making it necessary for the town to bridge the newly created river. If this were to occur now, no doubt modern machinery would be employed to quickly restore the river to its original bed.

About the turn of the century a turkey farmer named Jim bought the entire island and for years maintained his large flocks of turkeys there. Hence the name Turkey Jim Bridge.

In 1958, Edward Pattee, the "Road Agent" or "Highway Supervisor" of the New Hampshire town of Campton discovered that he had a badly decaying bottom chord in this covered bridge. He proceeded to change the posting, for a guaranteed safe capacity, from 6 tons to 2 tons. While this road and bridge were now essentially private, leading only to a motel, it had 100 years ago led to more properties as a public road, and its status had never been changed. Moreover, the motel owner was entitled to fire protection, and the 2-ton limit would not allow the passage of the town's fire vehicles.

The motel owner ordered the town to restore the bridge at once and remove the restriction. After a meeting of the selectmen and road agent with appropriate counsel, it was decided that the "little" town was in "big" trouble.

The State of New Hampshire has a plan for saving its covered spans whereby the State will pay 40% of the restoration cost and the town 60%. The State was at once called in to see what could be done to help. The estimated cost of a state supervised restoration job was $8,500. Of this, the state would pay $3,400, and the town $5,100.

To the average rural New England Yankee of any of the three northern states, the silver dollar is still a "cartwheel" and is deeply respected as such. If some folks of yesterday are said to have held onto the dollar until the eagle complained, then I think it is safe to say that some of these people await his second or third scream! I do not attempt to belittle the thrifty. They are honorable people and a stabilizing force in our society.

We were asked to attend two Sunday morning conferences at the bridge site with the selectmen and road agent.

The Board of Selectmen was made up of one 80-year-old proprietor of a general store, a middle-aged banker with business in a nearby town, and one factory foreman. The Road Agent was a younger man, a pick and shovel man, blessed with tremendous energy and the willingness to expend it.

We agreed to repair the bridge and leave it in good, sound condition for a lump sum of $3,500. In this case the town would carry the burden of payment alone and even then would save $1,600. The elder selectman finally said that he could not see investing money in an old bridge that in his memory had been beaten by several bad floods. This bridge was kept in place by cables fastened to large trees. In severe flood conditions it would float and have to withstand the punishment of floating debris which would be riding in the mainstream.

A railroad line from Plymouth to Woodsville, New Hampshire, had just been discontinued, and a local contractor had removed several overpasses containing large timbers. He had this excellent treated Georgia pine lumber of various sizes stock-piled in his yard, and would sell some at 6¢ per board foot. The market price new, if available, would be at least 35¢ per board foot.

We offered to build the town a **new** bridge for the same $3,500 and the authorities said they were all for that. In this as in the above-mentioned repair proposal, the town would be working unassisted. To qualify for state aid, if work was performed other than by the state, there would have to be state plans and specifications awarded to a contractor through competitive bidding and supervised and inspected by the State. This bridge would have met none of these required conditions.

The tin roof of Turkey Jim Bridge is jacked off and rolled toward the camera.

Floor system of the bridge is given some additional shoring before trusses are removed.

Alfonzo Downing who furnished the timber and a place in his yard for our framing operation arrives with the trusses for the new bridge.

The 60' trusses are just about a balance on Mr. Downing's small trailer.

The trusses will be rolled across the river on the old floor which will then be dismembered and removed.

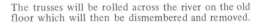

We moved our framing horses into the contractor's yard, beside the stockpiles of timber, and went to work.

The old bridge was a modified Queenpost. We made the new bridge to resemble the old design as much as possible to avoid the appearance of being a stranger in their midst.

The replacement trusses were heavier than the old. Where the old bottom chords had been framed of 5 x 12 inch timber, our supply made it necessary to employ 8 x 16, etc.

The new trusses were loaded on a low bed trailer and were moved into the field adjacent to the old bridge and placed in their correct relative positions. The final frame assembly was completed here.

Next, posts or horses were placed under the old bridge to support the floor. The tin roof, which was in good condition, was then jacked off and rolled out into the bushes, maintaining the same elevation. The discarded portions of the trusses were allowed to fall off, and were fished from the river. This left a clear floor on which to lay track across the stream.

Track was then laid from under the new bridge frame to the opposite side of the stream and the bridge frame was rolled across the river into place. By jacking up the new bridge from the abutments, we were able to remove the remaining portions of the old bridge via the river. The new bridge frame was then lowered into place. Flooring of this bridge consists of three-inch plank laid crosswise with a ½" spacing between the planks. This prevents any accumulation of dirt which may enter the bridge on car wheels by providing a space through which to fall into the river.

The tin roof which had been waiting very patiently in the bushes was now rolled into position over the bridge. Having fitted in posts to hold up the roof, the sides were boarded up using all the serviceable weathered boards from the old bridge.

After completing the structure, it was necessary to make a small gravel fill on the remote side. To prove that this little bridge (57' clear span) would qualify for the State's 15-ton load limit, we loaded our truck with gravel and weighed it. These loads, in excess of 15 tons, were hauled across to make the fill on the other side.

To illustrate the non-political efficiency with which some of these small rural towns operate, I shall relate the following:

The bridge which the town had purchased, though very heavy and at less than one-half estimated cost, could not qualify to clear the established red tape. Knowing that they were economically correct, the selectmen maintained a nuisance pressure of such persistence that the State finally cast aside the "red tape" and reimbursed the town 40% of their cash expenditure.

After being carried down stream 1000' by an ice jam and left on its side in 1973, Turkey Jim winds through a camp ground on its way home.

Turkey Jim moving back over the river.

STOUGHTON BRIDGE

BUILT IN 1880

When in 1959 the Corps of Engineers built a flood control dam on the Black River north of Springfield, Vermont, several covered bridges had to be moved or destroyed.

The Weathersfield Historical Society was successful in persuading the Corps of Engineers to save the first two to be endangered. We were hired by the Perini Corporation, the prime contractors for the dam project, to relocate the bridges.

One bridge, the Stoughton Bridge, was a multiple king post. It was light in construction and served principally the old Stoughton homestead. We do not find an exact age for this bridge, but a study of the timber would place it in the 80's.

One interesting sidelight is the fact that the present Stoughton House, one of the oldest in Vermont, was built about 1790. It also was moved out of the valley in 1959, at the same time that we were moving the bridge. The Stoughton House was built by that family and has remained in the same family until today. We finished the moving for the Stoughton's and placed the house on its present foundation about 1963.

The old Crown Point Road passed through this farmyard. During the Revolutionary War, General Knox stopped at Stoughton's farm for a while to rest his men and oxen. He was making his famous trip from Fort Ticonderoga to Boston with the captured cannon which was used to drive the British ships out of Boston Harbor.

When the time arrived for our bridge moving, and we were leaving the river location, no one who could make a decision as to its new home, could be located. Mr. Andrew Titcomb, an active member of the Weatherfield Historical Society, when pressed for a decision said, "Take it to my pasture. There is a very small brook there on which we can place it."

We moved it into Mr. Titcomb's hayfield, and unloaded it at the edge of a little brook.

Next, we built some very low abutments from stone of the original setting and placed it.

Knowing Mr. Titcomb, the architect and covered bridge lover, one can feel assured that this bridge will be well preserved.

Stoughton Bridge, Perkinsville, Vt. in fall 1959. Stanley Graton in picture.

Moving the Stoughton Bridge to Titcombs. 1959 — Perkinsville, Vt. At right of bridge is Donald Avery.

SALMON BRIDGE

BUILT IN 1875

The Salmon Bridge, though being moved at no expense to the town of Weathersfield, Vt., did not fare as well as did the Stoughton Bridge.

A location where this bridge could serve a useful life was found by the Historical Society. It would make an overdue replacement of a small stringer bridge which led to two houses. We took the job with this use for the bridge in mind. However, a town official with limited love for covered bridges, said, "No." He also said, "It should be destroyed."

After the Historical Society begged for the life of the bridge, they were finally allowed to place it in the yard where the town equipment was stored or parked. They suggested it as a place to get the town grader out of the weather.

After moving the bridge, we were allowed to salvage some weathered boards from an old barn by a good resident. The boards were used on the bridge. All the unsightly boards were replaced and with portal repairs the bridge looked "cared for" once more.

The next year a visit to this ill-fated bridge revealed that its friend had been at work. The floor had been removed and imitation brick siding had been nailed all over the outside. A good servant had been exposed to a shameful end.

Moving the Salmon Bridge.

LYNDONVILLE BRIDGE

LYNDONVILLE, VERMONT   BUILT IN 1873

In the spring of 1959, we were called to Lyndonville, Vermont, by a practicing physician of that town. He was interested in saving one of the town's landmarks, a covered bridge which appeared in a composite picture on the Chamber of Commerce brochure. It was to be replaced by a concrete and steel bridge, and the contractor had an item in his contract for its destruction.

At a town meeting there had been a bitter debate between those who would save and those who would destroy. The conservationists had lost.

When I called on the good doctor, he explained where the bridge would be found. The bitterness surrounding the fate of this bridge was clear when the doctor cautioned, "If anyone sees you at the bridge site and questions you, don't tell them I sent you there, for I could lose half of my practice."

We told this gentleman that to remove the bridge from the 8' deep river and place it in storage in an adjacent hay field was worth $4,000. He could find no sympathy at his local bank, however, and had to give up the idea.

Within days of the time for destruction, two local business men who had their own money convinced us that by using some money and some sentiment, we could move the bridge a mile through town and place it once more across the same river for $4,000. The new location was fortunately a swift and shallow spot on the river.

When the bridge was located at the new spot, our gain could be summed up by simply saying that we had saved a good bridge. I could appreciate the feelings

27

of Hannibal when he wrote from Italy, "One more victory like this and I will have to return to Carthage without my army."

METHOD OF MOVING

The river at the present location ran from 8' to 11' deep but was slow-moving at that time.

In order to build a track on which to roll the bridge to the street at the east end, it was necessary to place fill in the river. An opening was made ten feet from the end of the bridge, through the floor. Trucks were backed into the bridge and the gravel dumped to the river bed below. Two small bulldozers were driven onto the fill at the river's edge. These worked side by side to carry the gravel forward at 1' above water. When the fill had reached to within thirty feet of the other abutment, the remaining channel was left to care for the flow of water. This fill was only 24' wide to accommodate 22' of false work or track.

Sometimes, because of the need for a tight budget, one cannot provide the margin of safety which he would like. He may have to depend upon his skill, care, and an occasional prayer to supplement.

The track for rolling forward is being built under the bridge.

Two tracks were built on cribbing along the edges of the fill. At the new edge of the river, a timber pad was built to spread out the ground pressure, and tie the

29

two track ends together. A thirty-foot bridge of timber was then built to complete the track.

The day after our "wet" move this is how things looked.

The local people had been warning of the quick reaction of this river to even summer storms. About as soon as we had transferred the weight from the west abutment to the track in the river, it started to rain. The rain continued all day, and it was still raining at 10 P.M., when we abandoned for the night our task of removing some obstructing concrete which we had uncovered.

Next morning our fill was slightly under water, it was still raining, and we still had obstruction problems. A local fellow who did odd jobs showed up and offered his services. If our cribbing were to wash away, he knew the places where it would be likely to lodge and wanted to speak for the job of retrieving it. Here at least was one man with a definite lack of confidence in our planning or the elements.

By late afternoon, we were ready to move the bridge to the east shore. It was still raining hard and the river was flowing rapidly at a foot above our fill. As we moved forward, the river continued to rise and as fast as the weight was taken off the cribbing, it was necessary to hold each crib while it was dismantled and carried to the west bank.

The local utility company strung lights along on a temporary foot crossing which was parallel to the bridge and ten feet away.

At 10 P.M. and with 2½' of water passing over the fill, it was suggested that if our work was being undermined, our own safety might be questionable with the bridge well above our heads. This was very sensible reasoning, but with our insurance company carrying a risk of $10,000 on physical damage to the bridge, what would be their reaction to damage if we abandoned the structure and went to bed? We were convinced that it was not our privilege to decide at what point the company's

Crane in background has nothing to do with our work.
It is waiting to dig for new bridge.

Son Austin & I discussing:
Controversial tree having us "in the ropes".

Austin Graton (L) and Donald Avery (R
while digging up the tree.

Steering dollies around corner.
Pulling wire ropes with tractor.

Once more on straight-away.

Removing falsework after replacing bridge on river.

risk was hopeless. We continued to work, and about 2 A.M. the shoes and rolls of the west end were brought to a safe balancing point on the east abutment.

That day's St. Johnsbury paper carried an account of the move, together with a picture described as being taken at 2:30 A.M. as the bridge reached safety.

We had lost very little timber to the high water. By noon, the rain had stopped and everything looked much more encouraging. The river, however, was still rising, and it is doubtful if the bridge would have survived should it have been abandoned the night before.

Because of prior commitments of work on another bridge, the trip to the new location was started at 10 A.M. two weeks later. Though it was 130' long, we experienced only minor slow-downs.

Lyndonville's main street is both narrow and busy, carrying the traffic of one of Vermont's busy north-south routes. At the south end of the main street, a right angle turn had to be negotiated. We had built a set of steering dollies, 16 wheels in all, to carry the rear end. The front end of the bridge was carried on the center portion of the deck of a 60-ton, low bed trailer, which was drawn by a tandem tractor. To develop a "fifth wheel" arrangement and allow the low bed unit to act independently, we drilled a 2" hole in the centers of two 1½" steel plates which were 30" square. One of these plates was bolted to the low bed deck. The other was welded to the center of a bolster that consisted of a 12" x 12" timber 20' long encased in two heavy 5" x 12" channels of the same length. A hole was bored through the timber, and a 2" steel pin was passed through the bolster and the hole in the low bed deck. The low bed was then backed under the bottom chords of the bridge and made secure for the trip.

The dollies were built so that every wheel would move to the right or the left by the pull of a cable. The two cables extended back through the end of the bridge. When a movement to the right was desired, a small rubber tired tractor with a hook on the front would pull on the right cable and vice versa. Anyone who could drive old "Dobbin" could manage the rear wheels.

This method of steering was very effective. The low bed trailer approached the first corner and had to be concerned only with getting his vehicle and the front of the bridge lined up in Main Street. He would then drive ahead and back up, within certain limitations, while the rear end slowly worked its way sideways for 80' until it also lined up with Main Street.

During this three hour period of moving around the corner, we were very much restricted for space. The telephone company had stretched their cables and other wires to the limit to develop one more inch of clearance. At one point, the forward and backward movement was limited to 2 feet by a maple limb which projected between two bridge rafters.

It seemed that everyone in town who was not working was on hand. The police placed ropes on the shade trees to provide the necessary space for our work.

The wheels could all be kept on the pavement, but as the bridge rounded the corner, it would be directly over a private lawn for a distance of 20 feet.

The owner had a 6' maple tree right on the corner of his lawn. We asked permission to cut it and set out a new one. (This one had been scarred by the sidewalk snow plow.) The gentleman said, "No." He asked, "Didn't you anticipate this difficulty when you took the job?"

I assured him that if one tried to anticipate all of his difficulties, he would be discouraged before he started. "The bridge has to move over that route and one must trust that the Lord will provide a passage."

After agreeing to allow us to lay the tree down on the lawn and stand it up again after passing the corner, the owner asked if the tree would live. It would have been easy to assure him that all would be well with the tree. Everyone would be happy, for the time.

I think that in everyone's house there are certain rules for living that are "driven home". Our house was no exception. My father always cautioned us, "Never express an opinion unless you are **sure** of yourself." And, "Be ever so careful not to make that first mistake in judgment. If you have never made one, it is easy to inspire confidence, but having once displayed a lack of judgment, that confidence is forever lost. It will be known that you **can** make a mistake."

I told the man that we could not be sure. We could only do our best.

We dug carefully on two sides of the tree and loosened the soil on the other two sides. The tree was allowed to twist in its roots like hinges. It was lowered to the lawn. After we had rounded the corner, the tree was stood up again and guyed securely. Loam was tamped into the hole, wet thoroughly, and fertilized. Nearly ½ of the roots had not been seriously disturbed.

Six years later when we were working in Lyndonville again, the same man called on us to say that he had been happy with his tree, which was looking healthier than ever.

Though the Lyndonville Bridge was posted for a capacity of 8 tons, it was said locally that within a year before our moving date, an oil tanker with a gross weight of 50,000 pounds or 25 tons had crossed safely by mistake.

At about 3 P.M., the bridge stopped for the day. This was at a spot where a good traffic detour was available. If it went any farther, there would be no place to stop, and the trip would have to be finished that night. In this case the telephone company would not be able to replace their wires before dark.

The next morning the light poles were dug around and permitted to lean away from the street for the clearance of the bridge. After reaching the new position on the river bank, some decayed bridge parts were replaced and the bridge was once more placed across the river without incident.

The bridge was used for a new car display room in 1960, and after several other uses, now houses the office of a real estate broker as the last of the "Passing Parade".

Groveton C. B. about 1935. Starting to sag at center, eventually 18".

REPAIRS AT GROVETON

GROVETON, NEW HAMPSHIRE

Covered bridge restoration is a business that falls far short of anything that could be called a "commercial enterprise". One has a love for these old and deserving pieces of Americana or he keeps away from them. He employs hand power, 100-year-old tools and methods, and does not show disrespect by employing modern rigging equipment to do that which the builder could have done by hand. It is usually a case of how much money can be made available to do the job properly. More often there is not enough and there is unseen deterioration that must, of course, be properly replaced regardless of available money. This is the price he must pay for the privilege of being allowed and trusted to restore something priceless.

One day in 1964 I had occasion to pass the Groveton Bridge on my way to a rigging job. I stopped to sympathize with the bridge, and observed that it needed prayer as well.

This bridge was built in 1852 by Col. Richardson & Son. It is 136 feet long overall with a roadway 16 feet wide. The floor length is 125 feet.

It is constructed almost entirely of native spruce and being in a locality that supported virgin forests, mostly of spruce, the timber was of first cutting and excellent material.

The trusses of Groveton Bridge are Paddleford. The Paddleford truss is a combination of Burr truss and a very clever and refined system of reverse bracing. The framer of this type of truss had a good chance to exhibit his skills since this is

39

the most difficult of all trusses to frame.

The floor had lost any cambre it might have had. It was in fact sagging eighteen inches at the center. The arches were inverted and made worthless by a repairman's tightening of the arch-to-floor rods when the trusses had rotted off.

The view along the bottom chord shows clearly the 18" of minus cambre. While adjusting the pipe we raised the entire structure 1' for photographic reasons.

When asked if they intended to preserve the bridge, Mr. A. A. Potter, Chairman of the Board of Selectmen and a covered bridge lover, said, "We do, but we have been trying without success for twelve years to find someone to restore it. Can you do anything about it?"

A meeting with the Selectmen was held at the site and the visible damage was assessed as far as possible. It was late fall, nothing could be done then, and the Selectmen asked if the bridge would still be there in the spring. This, of course, was very uncertain, and even after we had agreed to place a piling bent in the river, our prediction of having a covered bridge to restore in the spring was still uncertain. A movement of ice in the river could cause a jam and endanger the bridge further.

When completed very little weight was placed on the piling support and that weight was left on wedges. If the bridge started to fall it might be held, but if ice came down the support would simply desert the bridge.

A price was quoted for what repair would seem to be necessary. Nothing more was heard until after March town meeting when we were notified that since the town's water supply pipe crossed the river in the bridge, the townspeople had voted for preservation. Crossing here was also convenient for about 30 families who live on the east side of the Upper Ammonoosuc River. They were saved nearly one half mile each way by not having to use the next bridge to the south. It was desired that we start work as early as possible.

In the spring the river was found to have changed from a low frozen stream to a four-mile-an-hour river six feet deep.

To raise the center of the bridge the necessary 2 feet before starting our repairs, a jacking position would be needed. We decided to build an island on which to work.

A hole was cut in the floor and over 600 cubic yards of very coarse cobblely gravel was fed through it with a ½ yard loader until an island 12' x 24' had been raised 1' above stream.

This was covered with a layer of old bridge plank plus alternating layers of 12 x 12 timber — forming a crib until within five feet of the arch supported transverse 12 x 12 timbers of the bridge. These transverse timbers also extended under the bottom chord and at 8' on centers. Within this 5' space, a jacking arrangement was set up and topped by long 12" x 16" timbers to relieve the bridge trusses of any concentrated reverse loading. The bridge center was now ready for jacking.

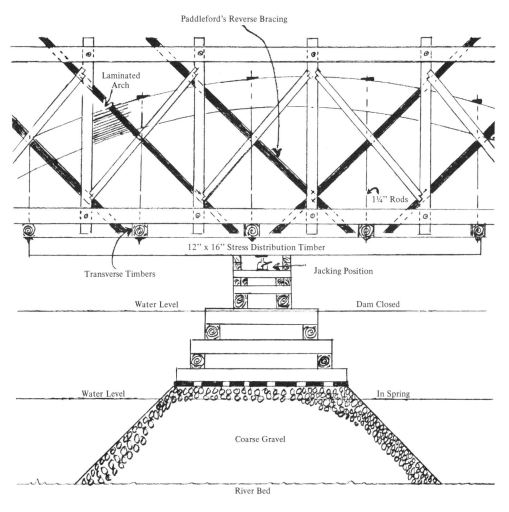

41

After raising the center about a foot, it was decided that the stress must be spread out more. At this time the local paper mill decided to close its gates and raise the water six feet more to accommodate an operation for removal of pulpwood bark. Now, with twelve to fourteen feet of water under the bridge, it became necessary to do any further jacking from the bridge floor.

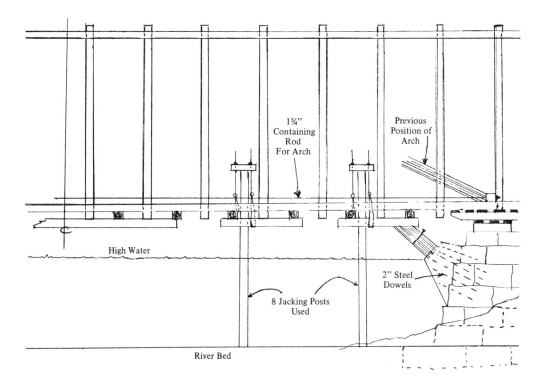

Eight pieces of 8 x 8 timber 28 feet long were threaded up through the floor, properly spaced, between the transverse 12 x 12's. To jack the portions of the truss between center and shore, weight was placed on these timbers, by using pairs of threaded rod which were yoked over the top of the jacking post and chained to the under frame.

This method worked well but was very slow. The truss chords had been bent for so long a time that they were "set". The ends would lift from the abutments instead of straightening. Time had to be allowed for them to settle down. By this method eight inches of cambre was finally developed, and when the job was finished, five inches remained.

Of a possible 32 vertical 10 x 10 truss posts, 20 had to be spliced. Splicing of these vertical members can be slow and consuming of one's patience. The top chord must be in turn jacked from the bottom to relieve the vertical pressure within the truss. Next, the bottom chord members must be spread to clear, in this case, ten inches. The post must then be cut at the bottom of the portion to be retained. One half of the post must be cut away and dressed carefully to receive the splice end of the new piece for a distance of 30 inches.

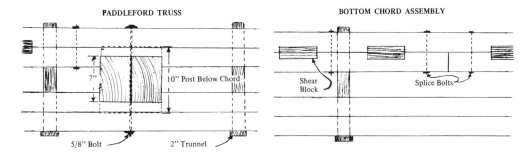

PADDLEFORD TRUSS

10" Post Below Chord

7"

5/8" Bolt   2" Trunnel

BOTTOM CHORD ASSEMBLY

Shear
Block

Splice Bolts

The new portion to be spliced on must be very accurate. When placed it must fit into the bottom chord and the two spliced shoulders at the same time. Also, the notch or dap must receive the advancing diagonal. If the top of the forward post has, through 100 years of pressure, compressed and moved forward then the notch would have to compensate by moving upward and forward in the direction in which the diagonal runs. In the Paddleford truss, there are reverse tension members which are framed together with these diagonals on their way from top to bottom chord. There is no permissible realignment of the diagonal because of the fixed position of the tension members at intersection.

This framing point at the meeting of post and lower end of diagonal is the "Achilles' heel" of this family of truss. It not only carries all the remaining weight to the center, but it is many times as vulnerable to rotting. Water running down the top diagonal surface is funneled into the joint which is more often full of dirt. This moisture cannot escape and insures the start of the decay process.

When workmen have fitted the spliced end of the post, horizontal lines must be drawn around the post at the center

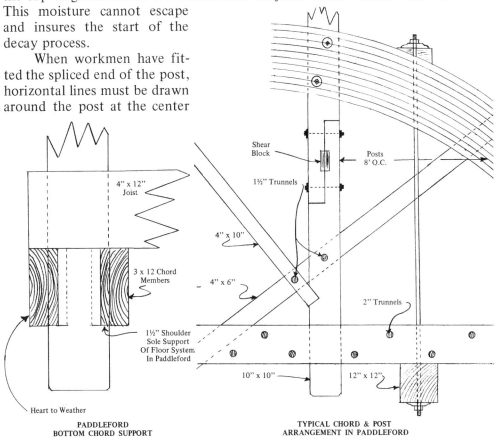

4" x 12"
Joist

3 x 12 Chord
Members

1½" Shoulder
Sole Support
Of Floor System
In Paddleford

Heart to Weather

Shear
Block

1½" Trunnels

Posts
8' O.C.

4" x 10"

4" x 6"

2" Trunnels

10" x 10"   12" x 12"

PADDLEFORD
BOTTOM CHORD SUPPORT

TYPICAL CHORD & POST
ARRANGEMENT IN PADDLEFORD

43

of the splice. These will be usually 7" apart, and will outline a notch equally in each piece that will receive a shear block of oak 7" long, two inches thick and the width of the post. The splice must be removed so that the framing can be done and then replaced. It is then bolted, using four 5/8" bolts with cast iron washers and the shear block is pressed into place. Since, even in oak, there is a definite compression factor in side-grain, end-grain must be exposed to the working surfaces.

HIDING A WATER PIPE

Not long after the Groveton covered bridge was relieved of its duties of carrying the traffic of U.S. Rt. 3 (the main New Hampshire route to Canada) the town had a municipal water problem. When the town's always abundant water supply began to fall short, the town officials called in outside experts. They paid them $5,000 to advise and suggest an additional supply.

While further expenditure and remedy was being planned with the experts, a local character launched his own investigation. He found that where the 10" pipe crossed the river slightly below stream bed, it had become uncovered. With this exposure to the movement of rocks, ice floes, logs and other debris, the water main had become broken in mid stream. It was a very high pressure line due to the elevation of the water source, and great quantities of water were being discharged into the stream. Locally it is said that there were many official "red faces" when this character disclosed **his** findings.

A new water main was promptly laid through the bridge, three feet from the upstream arch. This was insulated and covered with a wooden box for the entire length. The net result of this was to make the bridge very unsightly and create a serious decay hazard. Due to settlement of the bridge, every joint in the water main was leaking and could be neither seen nor remedied because of the solid enclosure.

When the badly decayed bridge floor and floor joists had been removed, we decided that it was well worth removing the balance of the joists and do incidental work to get the pipe out of sight.

This shows the leaking water pipe resting on braces above the floor. One of the inverted portions of the laminated arch is also in evidence, together with the bridge's 18" sag at center.

The water pipe was dug out on each end to the points where it levelled out after rising over the bridge. The valves at either end of the bridge were closed and several fire hoses between hydrants on the opposite sides of the river were employed to carry a limited supply of water while the change was made. With numerous slings and timber guides the 150' section of pipe was folded down below the floor joists as a unit. This would now rest on arch supported 12 x 12's. These would be protected from the pipe's sweating in warm weather by copper shields with overhanging edges which were placed under the pipe at each bearing. The water works ran new lead in the two joints which had been twisted and the pipe was back in service. The unsightly pipe, which had been the prime reason for saving the bridge, was now out of sight!

Groveton during rebuilding – 1965.

PLACING OF ARCHES

Many of the old bridges had arches that were subject to rotting on the ends. They were usually recessed into the stone for support and in turn were subject to dampness from the earth behind the stone work. More often neglect in providing proper drainage at the bridge ends assures the necessary water for the rotting process of the bottom chords, bearing beams, and other timbers.

In replacing the arches it has been found that the most satisfactory method of anchoring the ends is to cast a concrete thrust pad against the vertical surface

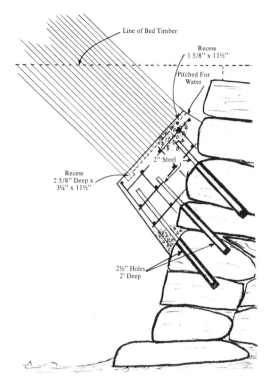

Line of Bed Timber

Recess
1 5/8" x 11½"

Pitched For
Water

2" Steel

Recess
2 5/8" Deep x
3¼" x 11½"

2½" Holes
2' Deep

of the abutment. After the location of the pad has been determined, two and one half inch holes are drilled in the face of the granite abutment, to a depth of 2' and on a downward slant; then filled with soft grout. This is a mixture of water, cement and sand. When the 2' steel dowels have been placed, the excess grout will be forced out. The top surface of the thrust pad is formed in such a way as to discourage the possible receiving of water from the top surface. The recess for the arch end is 1 5/8" deep and slightly narrower at the bottom than the arch members. The bottom 3¼" of the receiving depression is made 1" deeper to anchor the first two leaves of the arch while they are forced to bend through a predetermined arc.

The first leaf is started using a 20' plank of 2" x 12". On this is placed a 10' plank and each is carefully fitted into the recess after scribing. Then the process of adding a 20' plank to the end of the shorter leaf continues till the recess at the opposite abutment is reached. An effort is made to keep the scribed ends nearly perfect while the planks are carried through in a perfectly level position. The first members must be very accurately placed since any slight irregularity will be exaggerated as the building of the arch proceeds.

Beginning with the third leaf, the ends of the plank are drilled with five holes to receive the forty penny spikes which are used. The plank is clamped in place at

The leaking water pipe has been mended and hidden below the floor. One of the new arches is being built and the center of the bridge has been raised to produce 6" of cambre.

46

the starting end, bent to assure the proper location after bending; then the joint is "sawed up" and the plank driven from the top end. This process is repeated if necessary until a full end-bearing on the plank is assured. Then the plank is bent down to conform to the curve of the arch and spiked. When the plank is unusually dense grained or spiking is near a knot, a hole the size of the spike is drilled to a depth of 1 5/8" to avoid unnecessary internal stress. The spikes are then driven with the cutting edges across the grain. This will prevent splitting and increase the holding effort of the spike.

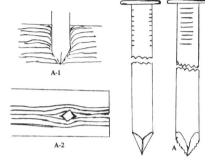

While many mature carpenters have driven nails and spikes for 40 years and never looked at them except to be sure to hit the head, they never realized that good, sharp nails have more character than a French Poodle. A good nail can be used with the barbed edges across the grain and not split the grain. It will cut across the grain and bend the end of the fibers down. This makes that area of the lumber more dense and resistant to the withdrawal of the nail.

The barbed point on A is properly used in A-1 and improperly used in A-2.

As the arch is built up, provision must be made for final bolting. It has been most satisfactory to place two 5/8" bolts at intervals of two feet. This will maintain the compression effort necessary to prevent the development of flat spots in the arch. Lines are drawn 2' on centers and perpendicular to the arch. As each plank is added, the line is extended, a template set on the line and the holes drilled. Thus, when the entire arch has been built up, the bolt will be placed without difficulty.

Immediately preceding the placing of the bolts, two clamps are used to compress the arch. These are made especially for this use and are activated by one eight ton hydraulic jack each, making it possible to put any 2' section under a squeeze of 16 tons while the bolts are tightened. Since dry timber does not lend itself readily to bending or spiking, it is preferred that arches be built while the moisture content of the lumber is still fairly high.

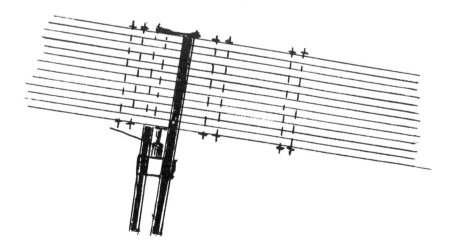

Hydraulic Arch Compressor

DRILLING HOLES IN ARCH

The boring of a fairly true and continuous hole is possible leaf by leaf perpendicular to the grain for the smaller bolts. However, in the larger rods, which support the heavy transverse timbers, the hole is not perpendicular to the arch. These rods are plumb. In such an instance, the worm would not be able to guide the bit at the start. The advance cutting on the higher side would force the bit to a lower position on the arch and also splinter the wood.

To bore these holes, having been careful to leave no spikes in the path, it is necessary to fasten a wedge of 2" plank securely at the start and finish of the projected hole. The splitting or splintering will be done in the waste lumber and leave the hole to be used more satisfactory. When the boring has started and the feeding worm has reached its maximum usefulness, the bit shaft is carefully plumbed. With frequent plumbing and due care, the 4' long bit will usually arrive fairly near the predetermined location.

After having painted at least the end four feet of the arches with creosote, the planks seemed quite secure from blowing rain.

The new arches of the Groveton Bridge, however, needed further protection. Though two feet above high water in the summer months when the dam held back additional water, the possibility of flood must still be considered.

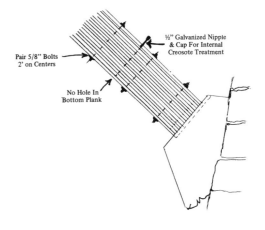

At a distance of four feet from the lower end of the arch, a ¾" hole was drilled in the center of the top plank. This hole was extended to the top side of the bottom plank. Into this hole was screwed a 4" nipple of ½" galvanized pipe with a screw cap. Now the end of the arch could be treated internally with creosote by simply removing the cap and pouring in creosote until it would run out between all layers of plank.

Although it is a very bad practice, many of the towns have had a second layer of floor plank added, when the first had become weak or decayed. Groveton was no exception: it had three layers. The first two layers were three-inch plank and the third was two inches thick for a total of eight inches of floor thickness.

As snow and rain blows into these structures and soaks into the layers of dry wood it causes very rapid decay and requires months to dry out. We replaced the floor with one layer of three-inch spruce plank, which we treated with creosote at all contact areas.

Several years after our rebuilding, a dam broke in the mountains above Groveton which sent flood waters over the floor and through the bridge. The only damage was the breaking of some of the boards on the bridge sides due to floating logs and other debris, thus proving that at nearly one hundred twenty years, a covered bridge is still young.

Groveton after dam broke upstream and caused flood damage several years later.

BARTLETT BRIDGE

BARTLETT, NEW HAMPSHIRE   REPAIRED 1966

The Bartlett Covered Bridge is the most westerly covered bridge on the Saco River. It is located at a point where the fast flowing Saco enters the flat lands of Intervale. By comparison, the Bartlett would be considered a very long single span at 182'. Though an exact date is not readily available, it is believed to have been built before 1870.

This bridge carried the Portland, Maine to Montreal traffic till it was replaced in 1939. Later it was used to house town equipment and as its condition became worse, it served as a shelter for rolls of snow fence. It was purchased in 1966 from the Town of Bartlett by Mrs. Casinelli for the sum of one dollar.

The property adjacent to the bridge was owned by Mrs. Cassinelli, who had been a teacher of needlework. She had developed a market for fine fabric articles and wished to have a small workshop to be used also as a gift shop. The covered bridge always had attracted many visitors and with this beautiful setting on a stream of clear mountain water should be a natural stopping place.

The bridge, however, was in very bad condition. On the southeast corner, the bed timber below the truss was decayed so badly that it was only a pad of humus. The bottom chord at the abutment's edge was removed by hand without the use of a saw. All that kept that corner from falling was a floor timber which was caught between the broken end of an inverted arch and a diagonal member of the side truss. When the repair job was finished, this point had been raised 27".

51

All four corners of Bartlett were rotted off and the whole bridge had settled badly. These are the jacking positions used to raise the bridge to its original elevation and to relax the ends for rebuilding.

To point out the damaging effects of neglect, I shall mention an apparently innocent condition. At halfway across the river, the bridge, prior to 1939, had developed two cracked or broken joists. These joists were 4" x 12". To make a replacement, two 6" x 8" timbers had been threaded in and wedged from the lower side to bring support under the floor. These timbers were three feet too long when the repair was finished. Instead of being sawed off at the edge of the bridge, they were left protruding three feet to a point where all the water from the roof would spatter on them and onto the lower truss structure. The boards also were not replaced on the side. Consequently, the rains spattered over the entire bottom chord and between its members. These conditions caused a great deal of rot. The two outside members had **no** continuity at this point, and the total tension for the center of the bridge was really on one weak member because of a splice nearby.

Working on the southeast corner of the bridge.

To correct this, it became necessary to create tension in a section of 40' to 50' of bottom chord at a time while the members were removed and replaced. Fifteen minutes of time cutting off the excess timber would have saved a twelve hundred dollar repair.

When some 20 vertical posts of this Paddleford design truss had been spliced and bottom chord members at all four corners replaced, the arches were due for repair. This was done similarly to the Groveton repair. The arches had developed many flat spots due to the excessive tightening of the rods which helped support the floor. The nuts on these rods were oiled and loosened to the end of the thread. Next, the arches were jacked up and braced to follow as nearly as possible a true arc between the last supporting rod on one end and the last supporting rod on the other end. (The portion of the arch that is not "contained" by the supporting rods is tangent.)

Three arch ends had become somewhat decayed from contact with the damp granite blocks, and were not now long enough after trimming. Concrete thrust blocks were cast between the abutments and the ends of the arches to assure a good bearing and sufficient length.

The fourth arch end was inverted and nearly broken off. It was almost necessary to straighten it. To rebuild properly the arch would have to be opened up for a distance of 80' to 90' from the damaged end.

Heavy timbers were clamped to the inverted section of the arch and tightened some each day to allow the timber fibers to reshape without breaking. In the course of two weeks we had the arch in proper shape. The badly deformed section would again be tangent. To prevent this section from leaving its proper position in the future, two 16' long pieces of 2" x 8" channel iron were welded together to enclose a well fitted 3½ x 7½ hardwood timber. This was then clamped to the lower side of the arch at the end and bolted with rods which extended through the entire arch lumber and the steel. From a distance this had the same appearance as two more leaves of 2" plank. This arch end was then fitted with a thrust block as the others were.

The rods, being thoroughly greased, were then tightened evenly until all came to a bearing, then continued evenly until there was a slight feeling of weight. The arches would then assist and stiffen the truss.

Since the Bartlett Covered Bridge is a very long span, the arches were of necessity quite flat and were not unusually deep. To get the intended usefulness from such a laminated arch any tightening of the arch-supported rods must be done with great care to insure that the arch is properly contained. Flat spots develop very easily.

The usual signs on the old bridges which cautioned the driver to walk his horse were intended to prevent the setting up of a sympathetic vibration or one to which the bridge could respond.

An elderly resident of Bartlett told me that 40 years or more ago, in the days of the then popular 5-ton Holt Caterpillar tractor, he had crossed this bridge with additional snow cleats on the track pads. The plow would probably weigh another ton for a total of 6 tons. He said he really believed the bridge vibrated 6".

A vibration of 2" would, of course, bring a tremendous shock load on a bridge of this length. If we consider that the suspended dead weight of this bridge may be 50 tons, the weight variations under extreme vibration could easily be from 25 tons at the top of the cycle to 75 tons at the bottom. The exciting weight may be so little as to be negligible.

The following spring we built a small 12' x 24' gift shop at our yard. We moved this the 60 miles to the bridge on a small trailer. Upon reaching the entrance to the bridge we found it necessary to let nearly all the air out of the tires to reach the middle of the bridge. The shop was unloaded and we continued through the bridge with the empty trailer.

Gift shop being installed in Bartlett.

Though Mrs. Cassinelli has not had much success in finding weathered boards to complete the replacements on her bridge, she still expresses confidence that she will.

The owner reports that the covered bridge and the crystal clear river are a definite attraction to a large segment of the tourist population. A dime on the river bottom can easily be seen from the bridge. With all the reports that one hears today of polluted rivers it is hard to imagine a river so clean, clear and cold that it is nearly sterile. "Stocked" trout are reported to have done very poorly because of lack of food in this portion of the river.

BAGLEY BRIDGE

BUILT 1807

Bagley Bridge about 1935.

Some years ago, I had read in a publication that catalogued our New Hampshire bridges of the Bagley Bridge. It was described as a very old bridge that had been unused for years except for foot travel and was now unsafe for even that. The ends had been boarded up because of the hazardous condition, and being hopelessly beyond repair, was only awaiting the day when it must give up and fall into the Warner River.

To me, to write off the remaining usefulness of so faithful an old bridge without consulting anyone is like sentencing one without hearing his witnesses. Should not this old bridge have a chance to be heard even through an interpreter? To pass judgment without hearing the full story seems unjust.

I had not been familiar with the section of New Hampshire around Warner since it was off our usual travel pattern. One evening I had missed a new short-cut around Warner and was surprised to see an old covered bridge on the north side of the road. At once it occurred to me that this must be the Bagley Bridge. It was getting dark, but since I might not get into this area again, I decided to go back.

From the description I had read, there could be no question; this was the poor old Bagley Bridge. If it would support last winter's snows, so recently, it should carry one more inspector safely across. I squeezed through the end boarding which was intended to keep those like me out.

A hurried inspection in the coming darkness convinced me that all I had read of the neglect and abandonment was correct. Only one point had been in error. Bagley was sick, terribly sick, but she was not hopelessly so. She only needed a doctor who was determined to give her new life. Since 1807 the Bagley Bridge had carried the Concord to Warner traffic until it was no longer needed in the 30's.

As New Hampshire's oldest covered bridge, and as one that had carried many notable people across the river, Bagley should be saved for posterity. Among those pointed out by a Warner historian as using this bridge were General La Fayette, President Theodore Roosevelt, and President Franklin Pierce.

There are a few other bridges that claim to be nearly as old, but in the process of their restoration or renewal, all but a score of the main timbers were taken to the dump and the result is a replacement more than a restoration.

In proper restorations, the decayed portions of timber ONLY are replaced. With patience and skill, a timber can be spliced and all of the sound old wood saved. To say that it could not be made as capable as a whole new timber is to admit inability.

I inquired of the Selectmen if the Town of Warner would consider selling the bridge. They thought it would be well since anytime now the town might have the expense of removing the debris from the river.

At the following spring town meeting it was voted to let the Selectmen dispose of the bridge in the best interest of the town. During the summer we were advised of the town's action and the willingness to sell the bridge for one dollar. They had been advised that I would restore and preserve it for the future and would not sell it to go out of the State of New Hampshire.

At this point the town had learned of a very recent law that made it illegal for the Selectmen, even with a vote of the town, to dispose of a covered bridge without a meeting being called by the Historical Commission. To this meeting anyone who wished to speak for or against the disposal could come and be heard.

This meeting was called for early November, and it was well attended. Some sixty people appeared to object to the bridge leaving town after nearly 160 years. These people were against me, but I admired their tenacity. The bridge should be kept in town and I would be all for it if they were to restore it. If, however, it was going to be allowed the disgrace of falling into the river for want of care, and all were to lose it, then I wanted it.

Under this law the town cannot act until it has been advised by the Historical Commission of the course that the Commission deems best in the common interest. However, the town is not bound to follow the advice given.

The Commission advised that the Town of Warner allow private groups 30 days in which to produce evidence that private money could be raised for restoration. If this could not be done, the town was advised to sell for one dollar. At the end of 30 days the head of one group wrote to tell me that it was not possible for his group to arouse sufficient interest. He believed it better that I save it.

The following summer we rolled the Bagley Bridge off the river. The roof had been removed by the State in the early thirties to allow **higher trucks** to pass through during a road construction job. It had been replaced carelessly and with poor results. One could have no sentiments attached to that portion. The floor had been replaced from the original so that it also could be discarded if necessary. The trusses were all original and could be moved as units to Ashland, New Hampshire if freed of the rest.

Since the character of any old covered bridge is in the trusses and lateral bracing, where the artist showed off his handiwork, that was the essential part. There was no lateral bracing in this bridge. It was so low inside that a reasonable load of hay would reach up into the rafters. There were no ties and the spreading force of the roof was contained by "flying buttresses". This was another singular characteristic in the Bagley Bridge. The timber in the trusses was entirely of pine. This was a dense, slow growing pine which was as firm as southern pine. I have never seen such growing in New Hampshire, but it must have been a native at that time. The trunnels were of white oak.

Although Ethiel Town is given credit for having invented that type of truss, it is evident that the idea of essentially the same thing was used twenty years earlier. Bagley differs from the Town Truss in that it does not have laminated top chords. The 6 x 12 solid members made a stiffer upper chord and would be more resistant to buckling under compression. As mentioned above, height would not permit of lateral bracing.

The lattice members which slant toward the river are, as they approach the end, narrowed in their spacing at the lower end. This produces the effect of a fan in appearance and while maintaining equal spacing along the top chord, concentrates the bearing pressure in a shorter space at the bottom.

While we were removing the floor from the bridge, some engineers from a

57

nearby road job came into the shade to visit and eat their lunch. One of these younger engineers observed that some part of the truss could have been engineered differently and would have been better for it.

I felt a loyalty to the ancient builder to come to his defense. He had built well but he could not defend it. To set my feelings clear I volunteered the following: "If I were to both write a book and build a bridge, I would not read the book and attempt to build the bridge. I would study the bridge and then write the book. The bridge has proved its worth in 160 years but the printer's ink in the book may not even dry." The young man had no further critical comment.

After roof and floor were removed, the trusses were moved into position 6' apart and braced and cross chained.

When Route I-89 was completed and passed within 200' of the old bridge, we rolled it up a 10' embankment and loaded it on dolly wheels on the highway shoulder.

A "fifth wheel plate" was built into the front of the truss assembly. When we were ready for the 60 mile trip into Concord and then to Ashland, a tractor was backed into the bridge as would be done with any trailer.

A sympathetic highway department granted us permission for the move which was uneventful even though the bridge trusses were 80' long.

It has been dismantled and is numbered and stored in a shed at our Ashland yard together with the necessary restoration materials.

DURGIN BRIDGE

SANDWICH, N.H.

The road agent called at the Durgin Bridge soon after we had started to do some bottom chord repairs in 1966. He stated that he had been concerned for some time in crossing the bridge with the town's heavy grader when complete with its additional winter equipment consisting of V plow and wing. This piece of equipment, they said, would weigh close to 19 tons. The bridge had always been posted for 6 tons.

When our repair was nearing completion, the selectmen asked what we would estimate to be the safe capacity for the bridge when we had finished our work. We told them that 6 tons would then be a fair and safe rating. "You don't think that your work has gained us anything?" was the next question. A look at the pile of replaced lumber soon convinced them that there was surely not a 6 ton capacity before.

They asked what I thought of someone's suggestion of two 5' steel beams being placed under the bridge for support. This should be ruled out on structural grounds, as well as that of photography and beauty. First, the two or three bridges before this 100 year old one had been swept away by high water. Now we would be restricting the waterway by 5' or 6' even though the records show that **this** bridge was placed especially high to save it. Second, it would ruin its value for photography. The only unspoiled angles would be the portals. Third, it would appear as an invalid that could not any longer span the river alone.

The only authentic strengthening would be through the installation of laminated arches. This would complement the structure already there, provide ample carrying capacity to the necessary 19 tons, and not damage the photographic appearance. The waterway would not be impaired.

Arches had been built into covered bridges from 60 to 100 years ago to supplement the trusses for strength. We believe some were "original equipment".

It was December and the town of Sandwich would have to be asked to raise the necessary money for the job at the regular March town meeting. This would rule out our doing the job because of our spring commitments.

The selectmen approached the Quimby Fund Trustees. This trust fund had previously been the sole support of the Quimby High School until modern consolidation had closed their school in favor of a taxpayer supported school. This fund now contributed less and had a surplus. They had money which they could contribute for emergencies. However, they could not relieve the taxpayers of their tax responsibilities. Since the town's new fire truck could not cross the bridge legally or safely, there was an emergency. The Quimby Fund granted the town the necessary funds.

The river was freezing over and there were heavy snows. Water from upstream was diverted and allowed to run slowly down the river on top of the ice and freeze. Ice of over one foot thickness was thus built up and work was done from that time without being inconvenienced by water.

About five tons of timber for the under floor framework was assembled on the ice under the bridge, drawn up into place and fastened to the bridge.

One arch was then built and the rods to support the bridge installed. The rods were, however, left slack by three inches. Having finished the river work that needed to be done from the ice, we stopped work for six weeks to await warmer weather. Before leaving, we decided to make some accurate measurements from the ice to the bottom of the vertical truss timber in the center. A sliding rule was erected, held tightly and marked. A truck load of sand was driven to the center of the span and stopped. A second line was then drawn and the indication was not over 1/8" of deflection.

This 100' long bridge which was in its 98th year had always been posted for six tons and the truck (a relatively light loading for this location) had a gross weight of at least ten tons.

When work was resumed on the other arch in the spring, the road agent stopped by. He said, "I thought I would stop to tell you that the bridge held pretty good this winter." When asked what was held, he said, "The grader, — I thought if it would hold with two arches, one should help some." We went on to remind him that in addition to the one arch being unable to help at all, there had been an additional burden of over five tons fastened to the bottom of the bridge.

Durgin Bridge — new arches.

Since the arch and truss have equally negligible deflection factors, then it is necessary to equalize the load. The arch could be carrying the entire bridge or the trusses could break down before the arch came to work.

To be assured that the truss carried its permissible load of six tons, a floor deflection allowance was made. Two 12" x 12" timbers were run the length of the bridge under wheel locations. These were ½" below the floor joists and rested on arch-supported 12" x 16" transverse timbers which were 8' on centers.

When the floor had developed a deflection of ½" it would have had its load, and the inflexible arched system would absorb any weight from then on. The transverse 12" x 16" timbers were tightened under the truss only to use the dead weight of the truss to prevent any deformation of the arch as the load passed from one side of the river to the other.

A study of the covered bridges at this site discloses that this, the Durgin Bridge, is the fourth at this location. The three earlier bridges were washed away by high water over a period of less than fifty years.

Jacob Berry, a very successful covered bridge builder (with today's evidence of his building principally in Carroll County), was hired to build the present Durgin Bridge in 1869.

Profiting by the experience of his predecessors, Mr. Berry raised the abutments so as to carry his bridge several feet higher above the floods. His bridge had not been reached by flood waters in 100 years.

ODD Jobs

THE GINPOLE

These pictures show a practical application of the ginpole. The occasion was the retrieving of a Jeep, complete with snow plow, from 38' of water in Squam Lake, Holderness, N.H.

The owners, Camps Rockywold and Deephaven, are said to be the only remaining large-scale harvesters of ice in New England who use it for practical purposes. They still have antique ice refrigerators in about 100 of their cottages at the insistence of their clientele.

The operator was cleaning the snow from a new "field" for

63

the day's cutting of ice when he accidentally went too far. He drove onto one inch of ice where the harvest had been made two days earlier. The operator was fortunate in that he stepped out just before the Jeep sank.

While this was taking place, I had been returning from Boston with a load of long 12" x 12" fir timbers. Upon reaching home I learned that a very disturbed Mr. Needham, the boss-driver, wanted help at once. He had engaged two divers, if needed, but had contacted two contractors without success. The weather was very cold and the ice was already too thick for harvesting properly. It would increase in thickness by at least 1" per day. The ice from which the Jeep must be raised was the next to be cut away.

I drove my loaded truck to the location (on shore) and we unloaded two 12" x 12" timbers in 40' lengths. These were arranged in the form of a V with three positions on wooden rolls. The ginpole was erected with the top directly over the weight to be lifted and guys were placed from top of pole to the remote end of the timbers to utilize their weight.

Our employers became more than suggestive that we send the divers down to attach a hook which was lowered on the end of a cable. We agreed that we should rely first on Faith and if unsuccessful then employ divers. Two minutes of "fishing" for the invisible, with only the hole in the ice to go by, proved our point. As the pictures indicate, all wheels broke through the ice at the same time. Even the divers were surprised. The vehicle had been resting upside down and the hook had caught fairly in the center of a member of the snow plow mounting frame.

After the Jeep was raised well clear of the ice, the ginpole mounting was rolled back from the hole in the ice. A 1½ foot thick cushion of soft snow was placed under the car roof. The Jeep was lowered onto the snow and rolled to its wheels by hand power.

The vehicle was thoroughly dried out and was back in service in three days. The pure lake water had done very little damage.

Other uses of the ginpole.

A PORTCULLIS FOR FORT WILLIAM AND MARY
Newcastle, N.H.

With the coming of our Bicentennial Celebration, the Coast Guard had decided to give to the New Hampshire Parks Department the old Fort Constitution or William and Mary. It was in a shameful condition of disrepair and together with the World War I brick Mine Storage Building and surrounding land, was surplus property.

It had always been taught that the real start of the American Revolution was at Lexington and Concord on that chilly April morning, but reputable N.H. historians say it is not so, and ask: "Why did the British dispatch their "Red Coats" to Lexington and Concord?" — "To capture powder and arms which were stored or hidden there by the colonists." "Where did the colonists obtain this powder (which was eventually used at Bunker Hill)?" — "It was obtained in Newcastle, N.H. at Fort William and Mary when the N.H. militiamen and others overpowered the small garrison and entered through this famous portal."

This, the open defiance of the King's authority and the removal of crown property, to the surrounding countryside and Lexington and Concord had humbled the King perhaps more than a defeat on his numerous battlefields at the hands of a formidable enemy force. Some of the farms where powder was stored are still standing. The might of the British Crown which was respected the world over on land and sea had been dealt a belittling blow and those responsible must be punished.

Had it not been for the brave men who had dared to make this attack there would have been no Lexington and Concord, and British statesmen of the caliber of Edmund Burke might have healed George's previous scratches.

So, the passage through the portcullis at this entrance had been unquestionably the spot where our revolution started. Now there was no portcullis and perhaps the single most important spot in our nation's history had that neglected look.

In 1974, the N.H. Parks Department asked if we would like to reproduce the device which had closed the main portal at Fort William and Mary since 1808, if not since the start of the American Revolution. We felt honored and gladly put aside our regular work to do it.

After a tour of the old fort and an examination of the stone work with Engineers Sullivan and Antonia, we were given a 2' weathered piece of chestnut timber 4" x 5" which had a framing location and one rivet. We were also given two German postcards of the "turn of the century".

Since there is no longer chestnut timber available we used oak. We did, however, locate an old 60' chestnut utility pole from which to hew the 8" x 8" guides for use in the brickwork.

In July, 1975 I delivered and installed the finished portcullis with the help of Engineer Rick Antonia and his crew from the Parks Department. A local construction firm provided the service of a crane to make the lift.

Later, when the installation was completed, a dedication was held at which there were several speakers including Mrs. Meldrim Thomson, Jr., representing the Governor; Mrs. Carl Chase, Chairman of the Bicentennial Celebration Committee of N.H.D.A.R. and several notable historians. About 100 members of the D.A.R. adjourned to the Pier II Restaurant where I was invited to speak.

INSTALLING THE PORTCULLIS

The D.A.R. paid for the portcullis as their contribution toward the fort restoration.

Since the 200th anniversary of the raid on Fort William and Mary came in December, 1974, a cool month in New Hampshire, it was decided to have the reenactment of the raid in October. It was a fine, sunny day and as of 200 years before, it was useless to fire a fatal shot. The Red Coats were outnumbered 50 to 1.

Photo by Joseph P. Copley

The Red Coats advance to defend the King's property. Oct. 1974.

Photo by Joseph P. Copley

As they near the portcullis the overpowering numbers of the raiding party become evident.

Paul Revere had ridden from Boston the previous day with an urgent call for action. With "Yankee Promptitude" and in less than a day the powder for the "Shot heard round the World" had been secured.

The D.A.R. since commissioned us to create, as authentically as possible, a bullwheel of wood for raising the portcullis after a "siege". This has been delivered to the Parks Department warehouse where it awaits further restoration work at the fort.

Lifting device for Fort Constitution portcullis.

FLOATING DOCK AT HAMPTON BEACH, N.H.

About 20 years ago, the State of New Hampshire advertised a job: "To build and install a floating dock at Hampton Beach." That sounded like an odd job and perhaps even fun. We submitted a bid and were advised that ours was about ½ that of the next bidder! It looked as if we must have forgotten something.

We built the 30' x 40' dock in our shop, dismembered it and reassembled it just above high tide at the inlet to the protected basin where it would be installed.

The plan called for a 5 foot walk to the gangplank. This was to be on piling bents at 12' o.c. Since we had no equipment for pile driving and found that our price did not carry any money to hire, we had to "improvise". We created a "Rube Goldberg" arrangement for jetting-in the piling. It worked well. We held each pile with a ½ c.yd. loader equipped with a 10' extension on the bucket. Four men with pike poles, borrowed from our local power company, had no problem guiding the direction.

After we had reassembled the dock, I approached a lobster fisherman whose boat was anchored nearby. I wanted to hire him to pull the dock into the channel and around to our location. It was cold, damp and blustery, about January 1, 1957. We had been impressed by his skill in handling his boat but he would have no part of our deal. He did, however, advise us how to be safe from the fast-flowing tide water. First, get our dock into the surf. Mistrusting the safety of our chains, we were to become alarmed and go to the Coast Guard to borrow a heavy rope.

This we did, as advised, and secured our dock. Now for the next move, our fisherman friend was consulted. We followed his advice and saw Coast Guard Capt. Smith again to explain that the lobstermen considered our whole arrangement unsafe and had suggested that one of the captain's stout little boats was our only sure way out.

The Captain advised that they were not privileged to do anyone's work for them, but that he would prefer pulling it around the corner to going 2 miles out to sea after it, if it had broken loose.

The Coast Guard crew arrived, and starting one of their boats which was anchored in the basin, placed our dock in a few minutes. When the tide started to recede we set up a ginpole on the beached dock and jetted-in one 40' pile. As the tide started to rise again, we quickly yoked the dock to the pile, as designed. It could now be held in position and the remaining three 40' piles were placed easily.

We learned one fact. No one knows his way around as the man who lives there does.

BRIDGE ON THE FIRST BRANCH OF THE SACO — 1955

This bridge job was let with the road contract. The round cobbles had rolled down the river bed until there was not more than 4' of waterway under the west end of the bridge. The 500 ton bridge was to be raised 5½' and the abutments raised to compensate.

We had quoted the successful bidder a low price for this item and we were to do it as a sub-contract. There was to be a temporary bridge in our agreement also. As we started to make preparations for two stone-filled log cribs in the nearly dry river, the itinerate bridge engineer came along and advised that supports in the river would not be permitted. He suggested that a 100' Bailey Bridge was the answer, but having no Bailey Bridge in our kit, I suggested that we suspend work while we would "think it over". Looking back at our childish performance it is very evident that neither of us was thoroughly mature at that time.

The Montreal to Old Orchard Beach route has quite a traffic load to say nothing of the contractors 12 c.y. dump trucks.

It was re-assuring when the Deputy Commissioner called the next day to acknowledge that one of his "boys" and I weren't thinking alike. He said that if we could tolerate the traffic load and keep the jacking delays to a maximum of 15 minutes, he would pay for the temporary bridge in exchange for that service.

We made it a point to see to it that there was no over-run in our delays by having all shims ready and distributed at the ramps before jacking. Our 600 ton jacks were running light at about 125 tons at each corner and we could realize a net lift of about 12" at each setting of the jacks.

After starting with a 6" lift on one end of the bridge, we would alternate with 12" lifts, first at one end and then at the other until we finished with a 6" lift.

We had constructed a 40' ramp at each end of the steel span. These ramps were made secure and hinged on the steel so that in an emergency pleasure car traffic could be allowed to pass over the bridge at any time. It was, however, necessary to shim the 40' 12" x 12" ramp timbers before allowing trucks and busses to pass.

On one occasion, three Greyhound Busses, traveling together, came to rest on the bridge and were truly sight-seers while we finished our shimming routine.

As a result of our being poorly equipped with long span temporary bridging materials we had done a better job of traffic control and had saved a part of the expense of a temporary bridge.

Bartlett iron bridge before jacking. N.W. jacking position seen at left.

N.W. jacking position in river bed excavation. Clarence Corsey 3rd from left. Others not identified.

One of two 600 ton jacks used on each end of bridge.

After full lift was made and set on bolster in preparation for concrete. New pedestal level will be at right hand of Austin Graton, who, fresh out of high school, is aligning bolt holes.

Shimming the bridge end on corner between lifts of jacks. L to R. Ronald Shaw, Roger Cochran, Jr., Kent Styles.

MOVING DAYS

A Misunderstanding
While relocating a building under contract with the N.H. Highway Dept., the owner claimed that a highway engineer had promised the relocation of all shrubs. "The customer is always right." This MUST be a shrub, so we moved it.

Former R.R. station – Crawford Notch, N.H.
When a new highway was built into Crawford Notch, it left this summer home on the wrong side of the tracks. Instead of building a crossing to the house, we moved the house to the highway. We crossed between trains with the blessing of the railroad.

In New Hampshire we remove a house on Littleton's Main Street to make room for new People's National Bank Building.

Heavy loader assists on steep Main Street grade and into side street.

It passes by and is supported to the new location on frozen ground. There are 5 rooms on third floor.

When, a few years ago, the very famous old Sunset House on Sugar Hill in New Hampshire was demolished it left, unused, this 25 mile view into Vermont to the west . . . . and this view of Franconia Notch and the Presidential Range to the east.

So, when this rich man's summer home with three chimneys and four fireplaces came on the market, and had no view, George Foss, an enterprising young real estate broker bought it. He at once negotiated with us to place it on his newly acquired 2 acre lot with a $40,000 view and a golf course adjoining.

POLAR CAVES SIGN POSTS

The well-known sign at Polar Caves once set in the south bound lane of the present state highway. When the State of New Hampshire purchased a new right of way they agreed to replace the stone posts. They were to be located off the right of way and 60' south. As an alternate the State agreed to move, "if possible" the **old** pillars which held great sentiment for the Polar Caves owners. These large stone posts were built of stones from the caves.

When the "if possible" became an issue the State called us for consultation. We relocated the pillars as a unit and on a negotiated agreement.

We were surprised to find that these pillars were just a shell and filled with cobbles the size of a grapefruit. We now had to move the bases also, to prevent the pillars from falling apart.

The earth was then removed from the bases to a depth of 5' and 12" x 12" timbers placed around both pillars as shown around the right pillar.

We then constructed a reinforced concrete girdle around the pillars above the timbers. Five days later, when the concrete had cured, we jacked the bottom timbers to a height of 6' and rolled the pair of pillars, as a unit to the new location. Here we poured concrete under the bases and removed the large timbers.

Polar Caves sign posts in May, 1935. L. to R. Clayton Evans, George Joyce, "Deke" Town & Clarence Corsey.

Polar Caves sign posts in May, 1978.

76

Reprinted From MANCHESTER (N.H.) UNION LEADER — Wednesday, November 17, 1954

Indian Head Project

Lofty Tower Is Removed
To Other Side Of Road

LINCOLN — The famed Indian Head tower, seen annually by thousands of motorists passing through Franconia Notch, and a familiar landmark on the west side of the busy Daniel Webster highway to all natives, is going to have all of them guessing come next year, for now it is on the east side of the highway although looking exactly the same as before. Recently the 100-foot 50-ton steel structure, which contains a two-story house within its skeleton, was jacked up and rolled across the highway as easily as a boy would play with his mechanical steel set.

Not a bolt was pulled in the tower nor a window broken in the house as it made the short trip across Route 3 on hardwood rollers running on two wooden tracks and pulled by a toy size tractor. A high wind whipping through the notch failed to sway the big steel far from the perpendicular despite the mobile base.

The move came about as a part of a major highway reconstruction job in which the new road will pass through the old location of the tower and the large gift shop and restaurant adjoining it. The latter buildings have been demolished and a new roof top motel is rising across the highway near the site of the new location for the tower. The view of the famed Indian Head, which legend has it was a lookout for Chief Pemigewassett will be just as good from the new location as it was from the old, it is stated.

The moving operation by the Graton Associates of Ashland took about two hours of actual moving time. Previously the tower was jacked from its base about two feet with small hydraulic jacks; 12 x 12-inch blocking was inserted, and the six-inch hardwood rollers under that. The tractor applied a small pull and away it rolled.

The new motel building is to be 140 x 100 feet and will overlook Shadow lake and the Franconia range. The first floor will contain a restaurant, gift shop and tower entrance. A 10 unit motel will be located on the roof, giving a superb view both up and down the Pemigewasset valley.

This new unit will complete the cabin colony at the site, one of the largest in New England. The site contains 74 cottages with fireplaces on the 300-acre development.

The Indian Head development was formerly owned by Raymond W. Gordon, who died in 1951. Mrs. Nellie Gordon has operated it since that time. She is to operate a cottage court in West Palm Beach, Fla., it is reported. John C. Aldrich is to be the new operator here.

The famous Indian Head was discovered in 1900 after a major forest fire had swept through the notch. It has been a rare point of interest to persons passing through the Franconia Notch region ever since. To make it easier to view the natural face which looks very much like an Indian brave with a long crest of feathers, the tower was trucked from Lewiston, Me., about 12 years ago and erected. It replaced a wooden tower which had stood there a number of years earlier.

RIGHT IN THE MIDDLE of U.S. Route No. 3, in the White Mts. is this 100-foot steel tower at famed Indian Head, shown as it was being moved across the road to a new location as a part of a highway reconstruction project. It took only two hours to move the 50-ton steel structure, which contains a two-story house. (Photo by Keniston)

UNION STREET BRIDGE

In March 1967 the good Yankees of Woodstock, Vermont called for a consultation on the building of a new covered bridge across the Ottauquechee River on Union Street.

My son, Arnold, and I arrived in Woodstock, and in ten minutes, Mr. Frank Teagle had a dozen interested persons assembled on the snow-covered Union Street iron bridge, which had been condemned two years before.

We were told that the bridge committee wished to have us produce a set of working drawings for a bridge that we would consider authentic and, at the same time, meet the load-bearing requirements for an eight ton capacity.

These Yankees had engineered their town meeting so that an article in the town warrant dealing with this condemned bridge did not appear. It was feared that the taxpayers might vote to build a modern steel and concrete bridge if it came up at town meeting. They had called us as soon as town meeting was over.

When someone asked what type of truss we would recommend, Mr. Ned Williams, Dean of Windsor County's engineers, said that to him there was only one type of truss, Town Lattice. "What do you think of that type of truss?" I was asked by another member of the group. I agreed that I believed Town Lattice to be a good type of truss and was told that agreement on a truss type had been reached and we should go ahead with plans. A firm price would be expected with the plans.

We drew and submitted plans for an eight ton bridge. This would be the first **authentic** wooden covered highway bridge to be built in New England in this century. (An authentic wooden covered bridge has few or no functional metal parts, perhaps all could be carried by one man.)

CHANGE IN CAPACITY RATING

This bridge was to have a posted capacity limit of eight tons. Since it was not on a commercial street, the local people did not wish to have any truck traffic on it. The vertical clearance need only be governed by that which would produce a graceful structure.

When our plans came up for state approval, we were advised that if the state were to invest money in a new bridge, it must have a capacity of fifteen tons. It would also have ample height for legal highway limits. We had designed the trusses strong enough so that the state accepted our eight ton trusses for a safe capacity of fifteen tons.

It was, however, necessary to re-design the trusses and change the pitch of the lattice to attain a vertical clearance of 14'4". (The state had suggested 13'9" to 14'3".) To produce a horizontal clearance of 10' at 14'4" of height, it became necessary to increase the roadway spacing between the trusses by 10".

The floor system also must be changed for double the loading, so we increased the joists from 4" x 12" to 6" x 14". Timbers 10" x 12" in 34' lengths were fastened to the joists, under the floor in the truck travel pattern. These by-passed by 8' at each end joint. Instead of the planed 3" plank floor, a 6" laminated floor was used. This involved the use of some 25,000 spikes to hold the floor together. The State also thought that the investment of $1,750 in pressure treating would be well worthwhile in the floor where it is subject to dampness.

We estimated the cost of this bridge was to be fifty-five thousand dollars. This to include a four foot covered sidewalk, which we later increased to six feet wide for a more balanced appearance.

The above changes represented an additional expenditure of slightly more than $10,000. These expenses were shared by the Union Street Bridge Committee and ourselves; each contributing $5,000.

PROCURING TIMBER

About December 20, 1967, we were told to, "Go ahead." January 3, 1968, an order was placed for 45,000 board feet of Douglas fir which was to be sawed to order in Oregon and planed one side and one edge for accuracy. 30,000 board feet was 3½" x 12" and 3½" x 14" in lengths from 24' to 42'. This would make the trusses.

The material for all framing detail above the trusses was ordered re-sawed from dry timber which we found in stock on the East Coast. We started framing the roof trusses, rafters, and lateral bracing system at once. (See W-1)

The truss timber arrived toward the last of February and was carefully stuck up in our shop where it could be dried with warm air. We would try to reduce the moisture content as rapidly as possible without the lumber season-checking. Since the lumber was full of ice, care had to be taken. (Change in moisture content produces rapid change in the width of a timber, although no change in length.)

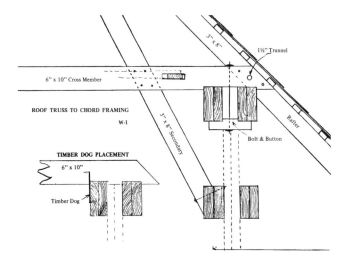

Owing to the fact that the old timber dog becomes loose with modern loading caused partially by larger loads and reduced space for knee bracing, we have devised and use a "bolt & button" system. This arrangement can be installed at both top and bottom chords and quickly tightened as the need arises. It is most adaptable to the Town Lattice truss.

FRAMING THE ROOF TRUSSES

While the timber for the side trusses was being milled and dried in our shop, the small roof trusses were also being prepared. Each section was laid out, clamped together and framed to a template. All mortises and tenons in the lateral bracing system had to be made and fitted at the shop. One ill-fitting piece could cause much inconvenience once it had reached the top of the bridge. (See W-1)

The several members are framed or notched together wherever they intersect, to avoid any movement from wind pressure. The roof sections were numbered and each member marked so that of the twenty-one sections, each would have its own relative members. These sections were built up in the street and clamped into notches in the top truss chord as units.

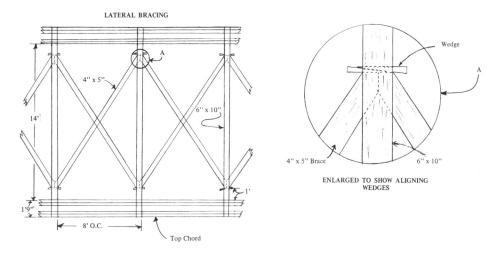

LATERAL BRACING

ENLARGED TO SHOW ALIGNING WEDGES

MOISTURE CONTENT IN FRAMING TIMBER

There are applications where the moisture content of a timber makes little difference. As in a post, if there is no framing and the only contact with other timber is on the end, shrinkage has little noticeable effect. However, where two members are framed together, the one employing end-grain will change very little while the member framed across the grain will shrink very noticeably.

In the case of the Town Lattice, the extreme factors of shrinkage are realized. If two pieces of 3½" x 14" timber were fastened together with four trunnels, when containing much moisture, each would hold the edges of the other to full size and each would split in the middle completely or split through the holes. This would, of course, render the joint and the timbers worthless.

To avoid this condition, all timbers must be reduced to the moisture content that they would be expected to have in two years. Thus their size would be stabilized. In the 3½" x 14" Douglas fir, it was believed that 16% moisture content would be the stabilizing point. To have too low moisture would also be harmful as it would change the alignment of the trunnel holes and reduce the bearing area of the trunnels.

In drying the Douglas fir timber in our shop (we had no scientific kiln dry facility) we had the timber "stuck up" two feet above the floor and with 3/4" square stickers four feet apart the entire length. The 3½" x 12" were mixed with the 3½" x 14" so that there was no direct upward line for the air, in the spaces between the sides of the timbers. The air would follow a staggered course and thus be slowed down.

Air from three burners was blown under the lumber pile, which was 8' wide, 7' high, and 60' long, in three locations, and shifted to different places constantly. For eight hours at night the heat was off. This allowed for the wood, which had been exposed to the heat, to regain some moisture from the center of the timber and avoid pronounced season-checking. Should the drying process with hot air be pursued too rapidly, the outside timber could be reduced to a much smaller volume than would ultimately be desired, while not allowing the center timber sufficient time to transfer its moisture to the outside. This would create a volume differential far greater than could ever occur in natural drying and produce a great amount of unnecessary season-checking.

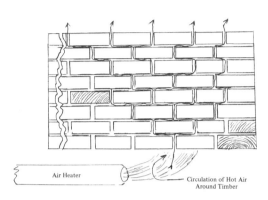

Air Heater

Circulation of Hot Air
Around Timber

TRUNNEL DRYING

While considering the moisture content in timber, we might well take a look at the all important trunnel. As in framing timber, too high or too low a moisture content at the time of assembly can be very harmful in the trunnel. A high moisture content would leave the trunnels loose at each intersection of the timbers when stabilization occurred, allowing the timbers to drift and an immediate loss of cambre would result. On the other hand, if the trunnel were to be over-dry and a reasonable driving fit, there would be undue internal stresses created at the points where the trunnels were employed when the moisture content has stabilized.

The quality of the bored trunnel hole is equally important and only the builder knows whether or not he has done a conscientious job of it. If the bit or cutting head is kept in an extremely sharp condition and the proper relationship maintained between the cutting edge and the clearing position of the worm, a perfectly round hole will result. The hole should actually shine when a light is viewed through it.

Should the hole be bored with a dull or poorly adjusted bit, the resulting hole would be egg shaped and only mildly resistant to the intended stresses without the loss of cambre.

The drawing will show the typical reaction of timber to a dull, poorly adjusted or even a sharp bit of recent manufacturing design, if cutting edges or ears have not been added.

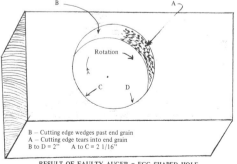

B — Cutting edge wedges past end grain
A — Cutting edge tears into end grain
B to D = 2"   A to C = 2 1/16"

RESULT OF FAULTY AUGER = EGG SHAPED HOLE

In the portion of the hole A the dull cutting edge or extreme end of clearing blade removed the wood. It tore away the end fibers to a depth of 1/8". The same occurred on the opposite side. At B the wood grain did not expose itself in a manner where chipping could take place but instead the bit wedged or crowded by, without going outside the intended limits. When area A is exposed to pressure, there is a compression of the high points. This will result in a radius increase of 1/16" at A and C while B and D remain constant. Thus the poorly produced hole, while appearing to be "good enough", would be 2 1/8" x 2" or 1/8" out of round. While we might imagine that we were correcting a faulty hole with a tight-fitting trunnel, we would only be producing adverse forces between areas B and D thus causing the timber to split.

Now, in 1970, that the Union Street Bridge in Woodstock, Vt. is completed and the resultant cambre has been found to be 9½", it is interesting to read today in an engineering magazine published 1½ years ago, an article about this Woodstock bridge. The author quotes me as predicting a resultant cambre of 9 to 10 inches or a loss of two to three inches. It has actually lost 2½".

LAYOUT

Before laying out the work an area was leveled accurately with a grader and a layer of crushed bank run gravel applied. This area was 150' x 30'. Across this area 6" x 7" timber in 20' lengths was laid out on 8' centers and positioned correctly to avoid any intersections where there would be boring for trunnels.

The plan of the truss chords was laid out and pencilled where it was to bear on this falsework.

Next began the slow process of personally selecting the right timber for the right place. Though most of the 3½" x 12" and 3½" x 14" planks were in 32' lengths, timber to 42' lengths had been ordered to avoid short splices at the ends. All splices were laid out for 16', so with four members employed, no splice should be nearer than 8' to the next. All joints would necessarily be two feet from a lattice intersection.

We had read of a certain bridge which was framed on the village common, in Abraham Smith's pasture, or in a nearby hay field. This is because, more so in others than Town Lattice, there were many pieces of timber which were nearly identical. The greater part of the framing on each timber could be done by a man in a distant part of the field. There would, however, be individual fitting when the piece was fitted into the main puzzle. Two timbers that may appear to be identical will have their individuality. Unlike steel, a timber which was obedient today, may change its mind tomorrow.

It would be possible, say with the Paddleford truss, to have twenty carpenters cutting and fitting pieces for a week before anything was assembled. It would be necessary for a level spot to be provided for each carpenter, for his saw horses, timber supply and storage area. Therefore, there was good reason to select the best level land within a reasonable oxen hauling distance of the bridge site.

In our Union Street Bridge the Town Lattice type of truss was used. This must be carefully fitted and clamped together. When it is once bored for the trunnels, there is no changing. It also requires less space because the truss fitting must be done in place before clamping.

First, a 42' - 3½" x 14" timber was chosen. This would be laid with heart side down so that it would "hug" the lattice and prevent a place for dirt and dampness to collect and also fit closely to the next member which will be laid also with heart down. If the sweep of the timber is such that it will resist the cambre to be developed, the timber must be used with ends reversed to conform to the cambre.

Next, a 26' - 3½" x 14" timber was selected and laid upon the 42' timber with the ends even. This to be followed the length of the truss by alternating 32' timbers. Each timber was laid with the same selection and care the entire length of the work. By employing three hundred clamps each made of two pieces of 2" x 3" hardwood, and two 5/8" rods, these chord members were clamped to keep the edges even at joints. They were also clamped halfway between, and at any point not alining perfectly. Two clamps were used at each joint to keep the members tight together.

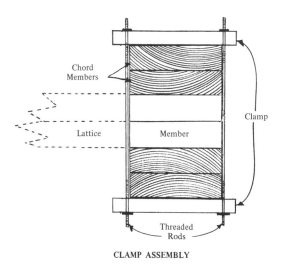

CLAMP ASSEMBLY

Having assembled the entire 140' of bottom chord, one end is fastened firmly to a stake. Taking advantage of any natural sweep in the timbers, half the cambre has been developed without forcing. By staking the falsework securely and nailing small blocks below the pencil marks for trimmers, the timbers, because of the extreme length, have been found to be quite agreeable to springing and can be worked into final position and staked at the extreme end.

To provide ease in placing members of the second chord, pieces of 1" x 2" strapping, in this case 29" long, are nailed to the falsework between the chords. When it becomes necessary to spring the timbers, the ends are moved into place with small pullers between the chords until they touch all the spacers. The timbers are then made secure by nailing more small blocks to the falsework. This same procedure is followed through the third and fourth chords.

Since the tension chords **should** and the compression chords **must** have a 100%

84

end-bearing to be effective and relieve the trunnels of the third and fourth chords of an unintended burden, a positive procedure must be followed.

Starting at each end and working toward and to the center, the joints are "sawed up". A sharp hand saw is run in the joints to the surface of the next member. This will equalize the width of the joint. While the clamps are still holding the members together to prevent their bouncing, a hardwood block is placed against the end of the timber being worked on, and struck with a 16 pound hammer. This will close the joint and if on examination the joint is not 100% bearing, the process is repeated. The joint sawing will alternate top and bottom member until the center is reached, then it is resumed from the alternate end. It would be difficult to produce a shock by hand that would close a joint more than 75' distant.

The base intersections of the lattice having been laid out for 4' on centers, a radius is projected from the extreme intersections to the top of the fourth chord. A measurement along the top chord will determine the amount of excess to be added to each 4' multiple without the inaccuracy of projecting additional radii.

The lattice can now be laid with the first layer being placed with the heart side up. When the timber is sawed through the heart, then the member should be studied and the convex surface be considered the heart side.

In most authentic covered bridges of 100 years or more, the chord is 3" x 12" and lattice is the same. However, due to the fact this bridge will be **legally** exposed to the loads that the old bridges were carrying **illegally**, we decided to increase the top and bottom chords to 3½" x 14". The intermediate chords were 3½" x 12". Because the stress in the truss lattice increases with the distance from the center, our plan called for 3½" x 12" lattice from the center halfway to the end and 3½" x 14" from that point to the end. This increase in width makes a more rigid truss and leaves a greater end section of wood where the boring is done for the trunnels.

The second layer of lattice should be placed with the heart side down. This will leave two heart sides toward one another, being necessary to get proper contact with the next chord members which will be applied heart up. The lattice being nearer vertical than horizontal in position, will collect less water and dirt than the horizontal.

The third and fourth members of all chords will be applied as the first and second except that they will be plumbed on the upper edges from the members below and clamped securely as the work progresses. The same sawing up method is used throughout the chord building.

Toward the last of May 1968, the first side of the bridge was laid out in our Ashland, New Hampshire yard and we called for an inspection by the State of Vermont Bridge Design Department.

Engineers Merchant and Watson arrived promptly, accompanied by the Department photographer Donald Wiedenmayer. After a thorough inspection of materials and layout, they stated that both met with their approval, and we were to proceed.

BORING FOR TRUNNELS

After the complete truss has been clamped securely in position, the holes must be bored for the trunnels.

A tripod mounted drill was built at our shop with a worm driven vertical movement of 24" and powered by a one horse ¾" drive electric drill.

A template was made to mark the starting place for the trunnel holes and so arranged as to cut the minimum amount of through fiber from the lattice.

The tripod would be mounted over the mark for a hole and the feeding worm of the bit allowed to enter the mark. Then the tripod would be moved about and a hand level used on the sides of the bit shaft until it was perpendicular to the work and the hole could be drilled with confidence.

CREATING THE PROPER BIT

The 2" bits which we had did not bore a smooth and accurate hole, so two were ordered by air from a factory in Ohio.

These had only 12" of worm to clear the chips and usually after being withdrawn for chip clearance, a chip would fall under the cutting edge and must literally be worn away before the bit could resume boring again. Much time would be wasted.

The two new bits were welded together to get an ejection worm of 22". The chips would clear and no withdrawal was necessary but the quality of the hole was poor even when the cutting head was kept sharp. A hole with loose wood fiber lining, though having the appearance of a tight drive, would elongate under pressure and, as a result of 700 such poor holes, the truss would lose its cambre.

Cutting edges or ears were made and applied with silver solder to resemble those found on small Russell Jennings or other small high quality bits. These were carefully sharpened and dressed to run one thread's depth in advance of the cutting blade. This was the answer to our problem. Accurate holes could be bored which were so smooth as to shine, as long as the cutting head and ears were kept dressed sharp and in the proper depth relationship.

THE SECOND TRUSS

The second truss was built the same as the first. Additional bed timber was placed across the first truss and in a position over the first bedding. Truss members were laid out with the top chord edges plumb over the corresponding portions of the first truss. Here, as in the first truss, when a group of holes is to be bored, a timber must be pressed securely against the lower surface to receive the bit-feeding worm and prevent splintering of the lower surface.

PREPARING THE TRUNNELS

Trunnels have been found to have been made of various hardwoods. Though White Oak is the favorite, some other woods perform nearly, if not equally, as well. Beech and Rock Maple are very hard, dense, and strong but do not with-stand moisture as might come from a leaking roof. Red Oak is more durable than these two, in that it will contain **some** moisture without noticeable damage. White Oak

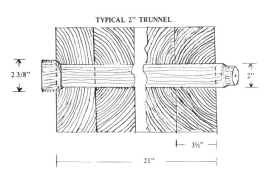

TYPICAL 2" TRUNNEL

trunnels, on the other hand, will survive moisture abuse, as long as will the timber in which it serves.

We have some trunnels that had been in use 160 years and are still as sound as

87

when new. Most all New England trunnels were turned in a lathe. There are many different patterns. Some heads were round and some square; some tapered larger at the head end and driven flush. A few have been turned with a taper toward the driving-end, and when driven, the head, though no larger in diameter at the end than the slight taper, presents the appearance of half an orange.

Many Georgia bridges used trunnels which had been split and then driven through a round hole in a ½" plate of iron. Though this method would assure the maker of straight grain in the stock, it would fall way short of producing a 100% bearing.

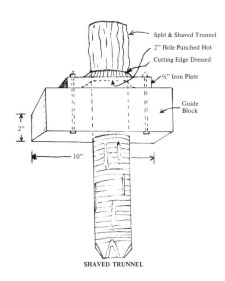

SHAVED TRUNNEL

White oak trees in our area are quite uncommon. After searching, on leads, over a large area we finally found some two dozen acceptable trees on an inaccessible hillside in a neighboring town.

We selected and cut the white oak trees ourselves while the farm owner dragged them to an opening on lower ground in tree lengths. Here we cut the trees into logs, which were multiples of our longest trunnels, and trucked them to a saw mill fifteen miles away. The logs were sawed into planks 2¼" thick. When the planks reached our shop, they were cut into whatever lengths would produce the best wood, from 11" to 27½". These were then squared to make 2¼" x 2¼" in the various lengths for turning into trunnels. Fourteen hundred would be required for the job, so 2,000 blanks were made to allow for those which might not be usable.

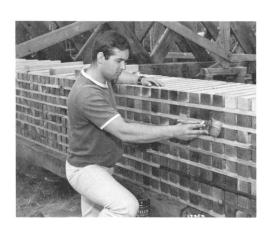

These blanks were "stuck up" outdoors in the sun and wind. They were separated in layers by ¾" pine strips and spaced ¾" apart horizontally. Thus the oak material, which is very stubborn about giving up its moisture, was given the best possible opportunity to dry naturally.

The ends of the stock were painted each two or three days with linseed oil to prevent end-checking or splitting as a result of more rapid drying at the exposed ends.

When the material was properly dried, we located the Walker Company which operates a small wood turning factory at New Ipswich, New Hampshire. These very gracious and sympathetic folks laid aside their routine work and turned our trunnels. These trunnels were turned 2 3/32" in diameter. After a week of forced drying in our shop, the result was a very tight fit in a slightly over 2" hole.

Whenever someone accomplishes something unusual with apparent success, he never does so alone, but must be backed by many helpful people who can "pass the ammunition". We have found that there are many of just this kind of good people when one needs them.

There was, of course, no shear value on record for a trunnel of any size. To establish such value, we arranged a test as shown in the accompanying drawing.

The shear value in this test and under ideal conditions for the trunnel was in excess of 24,000 pounds for a 2" white oak trunnel. The test was made in a computing hydraulic press at the Noble-Belisle Machine Company of West Lebanon, New Hampshire.

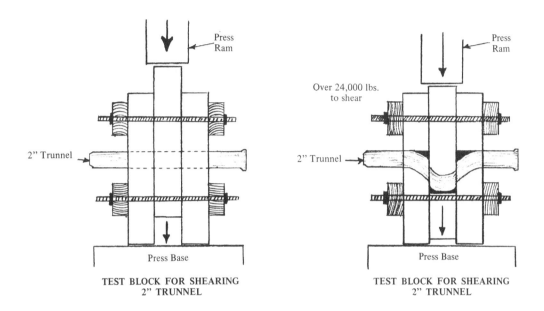

TEST BLOCK FOR SHEARING
2" TRUNNEL

TEST BLOCK FOR SHEARING
2" TRUNNEL

When the trunnels were deemed to have the correct moisture content, they were soaked in creosote to prevent any change till used.

The creosote would also discourage the activity of what is known as the Powder Post Borer. This tiny borer cannot work in dry oak, but if moisture be introduced through neglect in protecting, this little fellow can go to work. The net result of his activity is seen in some old furniture that may have been stored where damp. This fellow's work is imitated in antique reproductions.

NUMBERING FOR IDENTITY IN REASSEMBLING

There were upward of 300 pieces in the two main trusses, and no two pieces were identical, so it was very important that a positive numbering system be used. A number and letter combination was devised to cover the position of each piece. Our frequent huddles to decode the markings gave us confidence that we might well qualify for work with military intelligence. It was quite successful and every piece found a purpose at the time of assembly in Woodstock.

REASSEMBLY OF TRUSSES

The bedding timbers are leveled and laid out and the same clamping process is followed.

To insure perfect alignment, drift pins made of sharpened trunnels are used and driven into the holes which have been well lubricated with heavy cup grease.

First, two members are lined up with short 7" pins. Next, the first layer of lattice is pinned in place with a drift pin 3½" longer than the first, and the second layer of lattice is secured with a still longer pin. This takes place in groups located near end joints.

When the next chord member, which makes the fifth layer, is laid out, a longer and blunter pin is used which forces the first short pin out and replaces it through the five "layers". As the final chord members are laid out, the second short pin is replaced with a trunnel if alignment appears correct. From then on, trunnels are used in well-greased holes to punch out and replace other drift pins.

Before full length trunnels can be driven, a block supported by a jack must be placed near the driving area, to back up the timbers and prevent them from bouncing.

METHOD OF DRIVING

First, having made a snug fitting cap for the square head of the trunnel, the process of driving with a 16 pound hammer started. This seemed slow and tiresome and, of course, called for a **more modern** method, having consumed from 20 to 54 blows per trunnel.

Another cap was made also with a ¾" deep recess. This would drive the trunnel until the cap reached the surface leaving the ¾" head exposed as designed. This cap was welded to a short shank of steel which belonged in a small 30 pound air hammer.

The air hammer worked fine for the first 10 or 12 inches of penetration until the trunnel would suddenly come to a stop. The recoil of the timber was sufficient to absorb the air hammer blows. When the same equipment was designed for an ordinary paving breaker, the net result was essentially the same.

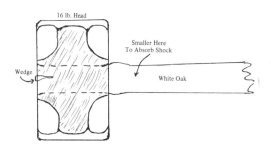

Since it was necessary to return to the 16 pound hammer to finish driving each trunnel, it was decided to use hand power entirely. Though the initial contact of the hammer might not be more severe than the air hammer, it has an immense reserve of follow-up, the necessary quality in any penetration.

It required about 1400 trunnels of various lengths for the trusses.

The shortest length was about 11" while the longest was 27½".

Two of my sons, Arnold and Stanley, laid out the second truss, drove the trunnels and erected it in about five weeks, without assistance.

"There was no easy way." **Right to left** Stanley E., Arnold M., & Milton S. Graton. Photo by Ken Miner.

ERECTING THE SIDES

After all trunnels had been driven securely into place, the side must be raised to an erect position while damaging or deforming it as little as possible. Since there had been built into each truss an initial cambre of 12", it was necessary to clamp to the bottom chord a series of blocks of various thicknesses. These would create a straight line along the bearing area.

Four positions were selected for jacking which would provide an even distribution of weight. Cribs were laid out and the necessary jacks were placed at these four positions. Jacking was started and continued to a height of six feet. Any further jacking might result in an unstable and dangerous condition, so it was necessary to take over from here with other means.

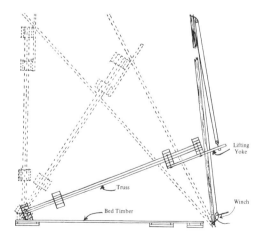

DIFFICULT WORKING CONDITIONS

This is, perhaps, an appropriate place to mention that in spite of all thoughtful precautions, one can find himself at a working disadvantage.

When a three sentence contract was presented by the town for signature, it contained no provision for trespass on either side of the street. We asked that this be added and a four sentence contract was signed. We now felt that with a four sentence contract, all must be well covered. This last sentence stated that the town would provide all easement rights for the placing of cable anchors as necessary for the erection of the bridge trusses.

We had reached the limit of our jacking when an elderly man asked how it would go the rest of the way up. It was explained to him, whereupon he said, "You would be trespassing." The fact that we had trespass rights did not impress him.

He said, "The town has only a two rod right of way. That will just reach to the base of the two 12' bank walls. Better not talk to the town about trespassing or you will be in a hornet's nest. Those who are opposed to this bridge are all right here. One has not been pleased with certain prominent townspeople; another has had unlimited parking in the street since the bridge has been closed; and still another does not want the street opened to traffic again for similar reasons. You would do well to remain and do your work all here in the street."

We wanted no part of a "hornet's nest" and could not raise the sides properly without trespassing. Even though it would be more costly, it was decided to take over from here with ginpoles. These could be kept on the pavement.

CHANGE OF PLANS TO USE OF GINPOLES – THE GINPOLE

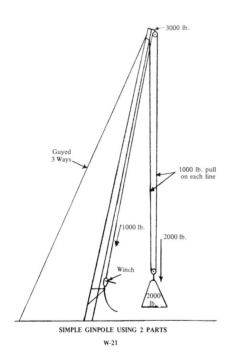

SIMPLE GINPOLE USING 2 PARTS
W-21

A ginpole is a guyed pole or timber that is usually erected in a leaning position and is restrained by ropes or cables. The cables are secured to the top of the pole and extend out to anchored positions in the rear.

Such a pole is placed with the top directly over the object to be lifted. To pull and lift an object safely with the use of a

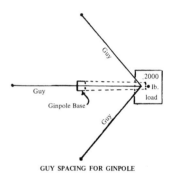

GUY SPACING FOR GINPOLE

92

ginpole, a line from the object to the base of the pole, if projected, should bisect the line between the two guy anchors, if two are used.

Usually, with this device, which is as old as civilization, a hand winch is used. The winch is fastened to the base of the pole and the line passed through the pulley block at the top of the pole and then down to the object.

By attaching the winch to the base of the ginpole, the force between the winch and the head block at the top of the pole is contained by the pole, and the only active outside force left for consideration, is that created by the object-to-head block line which, of course, is countered by the guys.

In the application to be considered, in the raising of the truss, there are no guys. A loose timber yoke holds the top of the pole within certain limits. As the truss raises, so does the containing yoke.

Because the weight to be lifted is two and one-half tons at each lifting position, we cannot lift it by hand with a single "part" or one direct line as outlined above. Two parts must be used to give sufficient lifting effort. The hand-powered device at the base of the ginpole will produce a direct line pull of only 1½ tons. (See W-21)

The arrangement of lines will be as shown in the diagram above. The third line, running the length of the pole, does no mechanical good. It simply allows the operator of the pulling device to work at the base of the pole instead of at the top. The stresses produced by this line are contained by the pole.

Thus, in this lift we start with a fixed or dead end at the top of the pole, run the line down through a snatch block at the lifting yoke, and return to another snatch block at the top. Here we have the two parts to develop twice the lift of our winch. We then simply descend the pole to the base where we can operate a hand winch.

The bases of these poles were placed in recesses in the pavement at the edge of the street, adjacent to the four jacking positions. Cables were run from the bases, under the added bottom chord leveling blocks, and up around to the lattice. This would unwind as the truss went up, maintaining a straight line without damaging the structure.

Loose-fitting enclosures or yokes were clamped to the top chord to guide the ginpoles as the side was pulled or pushed into an erect position.

It was then necessary to move the erected truss five feet further away from the center of the street, to provide the necessary nineteen feet for the assembling of the second side. This was accomplished by jacking.

RAISED SECOND SIDE ALONE

Having a routine rigging business that cannot be neglected, it became necessary to leave sons Arnold and Stanley, unassisted, to assemble and erect the second truss. They then positioned both trusses to receive the roof assembly.

PREPARATION FOR ROOF TRUSSES

Since the roof truss must serve in several capacities, it is essential that it be made very secure and close fitting. It must prevent sway by being held fast to the top chord and also being braced to the third chord. It must be equally secure against any movement along the length of the top chord as this movement would render the lateral bracing useless.

To prepare a secure position for the cross-ties of the roof trusses, a recess 1" deep and 6" wide is made across the top of both trusses at eight foot intervals. The truss timber is also framed into the cross-ties.

To assist in this framing, we were fortunate in enlisting, for a few weeks, the

94

services of David Howe, Sr., a semi-retired craftsman from the next town. With a substantial thirty-five year reputation for producing work that was faultless, this man's product needed no inspection.

SHINGLES

The shingles were sawed out in northern Maine, where there is a greater supply of cedar trees though much of this forest is of inferior quality.

The shingles were of ½" white cedar boards in 36" lengths so it was only necessary to use full 2" x 4" nailing strips, instead of boards on the roof to which to secure the shingles. The nailing strips were used 16" on centers giving the shingles an exposure of 16" to the weather.

Although these shingles were sawed to order, nearly 20% had to be culled out to preserve a desirable quality level.

PINE SIDING

The boards for the bridge sides were sawed from selected old growth pine logs. An old growth pine is a pine tree that has reached maturity. It is perhaps 200 years old. Since, in pine, the average sap wood portion represents the last 20 to 25 years' growth, a 50 year old pine might be nearly one-half sap. The most recent years would have been the more productive.

In the old and mature tree, the heart wood is dry, contains much pitch, and is quite immune to changes in humidity. If the tree had reached 30" in diameter and had nearly ceased to grow in its old age, the entire sap wood layer might be only 2" thick.

In preparing selected boards for a bridge, the sap wood must be wasted as it has a relatively short life expectancy compared with heart wood.

After air drying for six months, the boards were planed to 7/8" thickness. These were then sorted and about one-third selected for cutting into bridge lengths. They were edged in our shop and any "sap" wood removed. The ship-lap edge was produced by removing a 7/16" square section from the alternate edges. The boards were "stuck up" again and allowed to dry for two months more inside. The boards were then treated with a brush-applied coat of preservative and piled inside to "soak".

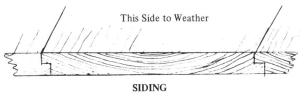

This Side to Weather

SIDING

When the boards were used, the heart side was always exposed to the weather. Since the natural curl is away from the heart side, the sun will neutralize this and the result

95

will be a fairly flat boarding without edges projecting. The boards were first fitted and nailed slightly with wire nails, which were later drawn and replaced with cut nails from a small factory on Cape Cod.

WAIT FOR WEATHER

In our planning, the next move was to put the bridge across the river. Consequently in early January 1969, work at the site was suspended because of river conditions. By early June the river had reduced in volume so as to make possible its being contained in a twenty-four foot channel. The sloping sides of the stream bed were leveled to about 1½ feet above the surface of the contained stream and preparation was made for bridging.

PLACING TRACK FOR THE MOVE

Track made up of four lines of 6" x 7" spruce timber was built the length of the bridge in Union Street. This was built at a level that would allow for passage over the concrete back wall of the West abutment. The bridge was then jacked to the required height and two sets of rolls, shoes, and rocker blocks were placed at the West end. Four sets were used near the front end.

Track was then placed at a height of 6' above ground in the river bed with 12" x 12" timber forming the bridge. To these timbers, 6 x 7 ties were added and four lines of 6 x 7 track. The same, was built the rest of the way between abutments.

On this, three sets of rolls and shoes were placed. Each set carried a 10 x 10 timber which reached across the two tracks. These served to tie the structure above together and reduce any side sway in the crib work immediately above. On these three 10 x 10's, two 34' 10 x 12 timbers were placed above either track to receive the cribs. Twelve cribs were then built on this bed and frequently tied together with 6 x 7 needles. When a height was reached where it was felt necessary to tie again, four more 34' 10 x 12 timbers were used as below. Again, several cross timbers of 6 x 14 were placed to stabilize the cribs which would now be extended to the elevation of the bottom of the track in the street.

METHOD OF MOVING

Due to the fact that this was to be the first authentic highway covered bridge in New England, at least in this century, it should surely be moved by means of the appropriate period.

We had a capstan, blocks and 600' of 1½" line. The only ingredient lacking seemed to be the motive power and this was found in the names of Ben and Joe, two prize winning oxen that lived five miles to the South. Having consulted with their owner, it was agreed that they would come to our rescue and lend the touch of antiquity. It was also agreed that they would "come to work" the day before and walk around the capstan. This was to make sure they did not lend a **modern**

look at the appointed time and refuse to **labor** under our **working conditions**. Ben and Joe, however, saw nothing wrong with conditions or fringe benefits. Every child after petting the one ton oxen would offer some dry hay.

We had a 600 foot length of rope and since we were using two quadruple blocks and nine parts were involved, a working length of 55 feet was the limit.

To prepare to move an object such as this bridge the two "blocks" are laid out and the rope is fastened at the dead end to the head block. It is then passed around the other block and returned till all pulleys are occupied and then passes to the capstan on the opposite side of the river from the bridge.

The capstan, by winding the rope on a 10" wheel, gives the oxen a ten to one advantage. If we then multiply

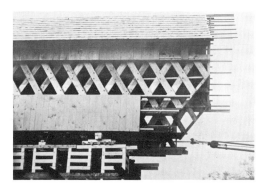

this advantage by the nine parts of rope involved, we would have a 90 to 1 advantage. If we were to disregard friction, which is relatively high in crude devices such as this, the one yoke of oxen could pull as much as ninety yoke or 180 oxen.

This will give one some idea why our ancestors were able to move many seemingly impossible objects with so little.

On June 29, the day the move was to start at 10 A.M., the oxen were ready but patient. They accepted, from the pre-school crowd, head scratching and even nose twisting with a friendly appreciation.

As usual, there was more to do in preparation and it was 2 P.M. before Ben and Joe could actually go to work. They started their slow course around the capstan with a net yield, at the bridge across the river, of 3½" per complete turn of the sweep. A forward movement of 16 feet was recorded at 5 P.M. when Ben and Joe started back for the pasture.

Because of the low track, the movement forward had brought our first set of rolls up against the abutment wall. That evening we jacked the front end of the bridge and reset that first set of rolls in front of the concrete wall.

On the first day, the Union Street Bridge Committee had placed 100 chairs on the lawn of an adjacent house. These were occupied all day with an even greater number of people in the street at all times. The weather was ideal. That this bridge moving was an unusual and interesting event was evidenced by the untold number of cameras in action, and photography seemed to be at its best. The press and construction periodicals were well represented also. It was no time for a "mistake". It would be too well documented!

The second day was also ideal with equally large crowds. Ben and Joe started their day at 10:30 A.M. and with stops to jack the second set of rolls over the wall,

we had gained 46 feet when they quit. The day was uneventful except for progress. The bridge had now moved a total of 62' from the start.

At the start, while setting up the capstan, we had spread 6" of clay bearing sand on the pavement and wet it down to make it easier for the unshod oxen. It would also prevent them from slipping.

Each time the bridge was pulled ahead 25 or 30 feet, the blocks were that much nearer each other. Two boys in the bridge would pull the head block back toward the bridge with two 1½ ton come-alongs. This would pull all the rope back through the works leaving only enough for the boy who maintained the tension on the capstan.

The third day, many people thought the oxen should have a rest after their monotonous circular pulling, so we substituted our truck winch for the capstan and started moving the bridge forward again. There was much disappointment expressed by photographers and other onlookers. These were a new group of camera and covered bridge people. They had been in Pennsylvania, Ohio, Maine, etc. when we were using the oxen. "The show" was incomplete and they were having less then their neighbors had!

We promised to get Ben and Joe back for the next day. There would be enough work left to last all day since the last set of rolls must be jacked over the wall.

The next day all possible cooperation was provided for **complete** photography and observation. At three P.M. the bridge was within three feet of its destination. It was necessary for accuracy to relieve the oxen and move the rest of the way ahead by hand power. If we moved too fast and were inaccurate, we might have to back the bridge up and come ahead again to inch into the proper position. Now it was a slight relief to know that even with a sudden rise of the water, we could support the bridge on the abutments and at most lose only the river full of timbers.

101

LOWERING INTO POSITION

Because of the space required for timber, shoes, rolls, and track, the bridge had to pass over the end wall at four feet above final position on the West end. The East end abutment was two feet higher to accommodate the grade of the street and called for a lowering of but two feet there.

Although very strong in working position, this type of truss is quite difficult to jack. It is vulnerable to a concentration of pressure along the bottom chord. Damage could be done in shearing trunnels and it could not be seen, so it is necessary to jack from several points at once, and have transfer members to carry some of the pressure to the next chord above.

Much accuracy can be attained by hand work even in the handling of very heavy objects. One need only to study the physical reactions to his certain moves and he can anticipate, in close tolerances, the net result.

Thus, when an object such as this bridge end, with an accumulated weight of 40 tons on 24' of spongy cribbing, is to be moved from side to side, little difficulty is experienced. If in lowering the object, which in this case is rigid, a movement upstream is desired, then the jacks on that side are required to retain a greater load. This in turn compresses the columns of cribbing on that side and creates a leaning motion. If this loading is kept constant, the bridge will be delivered in an upstream direction.

Should this not produce sufficient movement, the bridge can be rested on the abutment, the cribbing released of weight and allowed to straighten; then the same jacking procedure is followed again.

The bearing positions on the abutments were so arranged that the entire bridge would rest on four concrete pedestals 14 inches above the floor of the bearing recess. The pedestals were two feet wide and three feet long. A layer of waterproofing was spread on the pedestal to prevent dampness from entering the timbers from below. The pedestal was then covered with four pieces of dried and creosoted oak 3" x 8" two feet long spaced evenly. Two pieces of 10" x 16" fourteen feet long were then placed on the pedestal with edges up. Two pieces of 3" x 8" two feet long were arranged under each lattice intersection. The intersections were cut flush with the bottom of the chord.

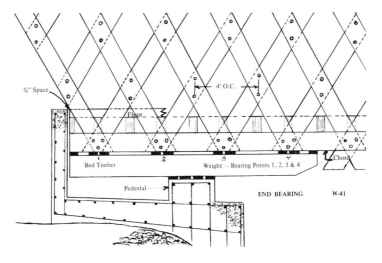

102

ELIMINATION OF DIRT POCKETS

Because dampness and dirt are the enemies of this vital part of a covered bridge, a place for either was eliminated.

In taking advantage of the shortcomings found in numerous early bridges, where inaccessible pockets would accumulate dust and dampness, we built, having in mind that compressed air could be used to prevent dust build-up.

The word "shortcoming" is not used disrespectfully for these builders excelled on all counts.

LIFE EXPECTANCY

It is a simple matter of life expectancy. A bridge which they built for a life of 50 years (average life due to floods) would be **expected** to need restoring at 100 or 125 years.

There is one bridge in Newport, New Hampshire, built in 1835, which has a posted capacity of six tons. This bridge is taking in stride loaded transit mixers, when the need requires. These vehicles, though loaded to only one-half capacity, have a gross weight of 45,000 pounds or a simple 22½ tons. This at the advanced age of 135 years. Could this be equalled with steel?

I believe that for limited loads (perhaps ten tons) and a reasonably light traffic flow, over a 100 year period, the covered bridge is by far the cheapest stream crossing. It also lends much to the beauty of the countryside.

DISTRIBUTION OF DEAD WEIGHT

Of the four weight-bearing points at either corner, the two center ones ride almost plumb over the pedestal. (See W-41)

The theory of a long end bearing on this type of truss is in error. Since the river end of the bearing timber can bear weight but for a short time, it leaves only the end single lattice to add support on a long bearing.

It is impossible to obtain or develop a uniform pressure over these three points and therefore if **any** pressure is brought on the last support, it is bound to be excessive. A three foot bearing can be carefully shimmed to develop a fairly uniform bearing.

CLEARING THE RIVER

When the bridge had been set in its final position, the crib-work structure was on the East side of the river. The only access to the river bed was from the West side so the rolling action at the base was reversed. The entire supporting structure was pulled back to the West side where it was dismantled and trucked home to storage.

Then, in the early morning hours and while most photographers were still sleeping, we quietly moved a bulldozer back into the river bed. As mentioned before, a bulldozer had been used to level the river bed and narrow the stream depression for bridging. This stony material had to be moved back to its original location to widen the stream and protect the banks from being washed away by high water.

FINISHING THE BRIDGE

The floor joists were of 6 x 14 Douglas fir timber. These were spaced two feet on centers. One-half of the joists were 16' long and the others 24' long. The short joists rested only on the inside members of the bottom chord, while the longer ones reached across the entire chord on one side and projected six feet outside the truss on the other. This would afford support for the sidewalk each four feet.

Since the roof on the sidewalk side has an unsupported overhang of eight feet, posts eight feet apart were erected along the edge of the sidewalk to support the roof from the floor.

To stiffen the floor and spread out the load, two lines of 10 x 12 timber in 34' lengths are fastened to the underside of the floor joists in the line of normal truck travel. The timbers by-pass one another by at least eight feet at each splice to eliminate "hinging" at the splices. Thus a springy floor that would be absolutely safe for a load of two tons, without stiffening, might be reasonably safe for two and one-half tons after stiffening.

This bridge has a six inch floor of laminated 2" x 6" softwood. Such a floor of pressure treated lumber is, when properly laid, nearly equal to a floor of 4" x 10" oak in long lengths. When carefully nailed or spiked with cutting edges across the grain, no serious splitting can result from the internal pressures. The floor was laid with a ¾" clearance at all points adjacent to the roadway. It has also 1 5/8" floor openings along the sides where dirt can fall clear. The sidewalk floor is of 2" x 12" Douglas fir in twenty-foot lengths. It is six feet wide, and supported on projecting 6" x 14" joists which are four feet on centers.

CONCLUSION

In order to place our new Union Street Bridge over the Ottauquechee River, it had been necessary to remove the old iron bridge. Actually, though the corrugated steel deck was rusted out, as were the steel joists, the frame of this 90-year old iron bridge was absolutely free from scale. It was with a substantial feeling of guilt that we cut it down.

In conclusion, I could quote a very successful New England bridge contractor (the other kind of bridge) who, after reading a report on the Union Street Bridge in an engineering publication, said, "Milton, in removing a metal bridge and replacing it with a wooden bridge, you have made bridge building history. It may not have occurred before, and I would congratulate you."

I enjoyed this once-in-a-lifetime opportunity to create something out of the past; something that is looked forward to but seldom happens. However, it was a long, tiring process and when I finished, it reminded me of the Maine potato farmer. He had worked hard all summer, harvested his crop, and now had taken his last load of potatoes to Bucksport. Feeling relieved, he said to his friend, "Now I am going to Bangor and get drunk, and how I dread it!"

Photo by Harlen Persinger, the Webb Co. St. Paul, Minn.

When this picture was taken the structure had been partially sand blasted and quite well cleaned up. It was still open for **light** traffic including the town's two yard loader.

The bridge was well soaked with gasoline and ignited by local arsonists on May 11, 1974 while the local fire department was holding its annual ball.

In spite of the timing and the intense heat the firemen are credited with extinguishing the fire in little more than twenty minutes. This was a remarkable showing since they had to fight the fire primarily from the river below. The arsonists received suspended sentences.

Woodstock is the seat of county government and outdoor recreation. So, if you are an international banker or skier leaving the comfort of the famous Woodstock Inn or if you are an eighty-two year old lady who has just paid a $15 fine at the county court house for driving a three wheeled golf cart at 5 m.p.h. without a crash helmet, you will feel the freedom of the nineteenth century as you approach Woodstock's "close-in" covered bridge.

Photo by Richard Roy

Upon entering you will see at the right this placque, the handiwork of one of the town's chief benefactors.

Photo by Richard Roy

Designed and built in 1968-69 by

Milton Gräton and his two sons
of Ashland, New Hampshire

the first authentic highway covered bridge
to be built in Vt. & N.H. in this century
utilizing the truss patented by
Ithiel Town in 1820

Burned · 11 May 1974
Rebuilt in 1976 by Gräton Associates

Photo by Richard Roy

In passing back through the bridge you will get another view of the court house and you may see the damaging snow which has so neglectfully been left in the bridge and ask your local escort, "If this bridge is so respected as to have a picture in the Department of Transportation in Washington, D.C. or in the Governor's Office, why isn't it cared for better and the snow kept out?" Your answer would be, no doubt, as follows:

"Mr. Vilas, the old town character and the only person who will shovel snow, has perhaps balked. He is sensitive about the thought of anyone trying to beat him and will not work in such a situation till the next round of inflation, when he feels that he will be able to get the pay that he deserves. Being religious, he feels no guilt as sooner or later the Lord will take away the snow if the stingy are patient."

As you look down to the west end you will **guess** that it is one P.M. and already you are **sure** that it is Feb. 15th by the length of the silhouette on the floor.

Photo by Richard Roy

You may wish to stroll about on the west side. If so, at the first turn to the right you will find five houses beside the river. They are fine old structures, the fifth of which was the setting of "Dr. Cook's Garden" in which Bing Crosby was cast as an old doctor who was wicked.

Photo by Richard Roy

Baltimore Bridge, N. Springfield, Vt. on road to the Village of Baltimore. Its "relatively" good condition indicates a dating of about 1950. Built in 1870 by Granville Leland & Dennis Allen.

BALTIMORE BRIDGE

SPRINGFIELD, VERMONT   BUILT 1870

About 1967 it was decided that the badly twisted bridge was no longer safe to be used. We were asked for a price for making it safe again but at a town meeting it was decided that our price **was not high enough**. The matter stood for two years. The water from the roof dripped into the bottom chord on alternate corners.

In 1969 a committee was formed and headed by former U.S. Senator Flanders. The aim of this group was to restore the Baltimore and place it beside the Eureka School House (Vermont's oldest) on the east approach to Springfield.

The Eureka School House is said to have been taken down years before by Senator Flanders and stored in his barn when its condition became critical. It had been set up and restored about 1967.

We agreed to do that which needed to be done for the lump sum of $10,000. However, before we had signed an agreement, the committee suggested increasing the price to $10,500.

Though the bridge was in very bad condition and required much work, we found it pleasant and enjoyable working with those fine people who did as they had agreed, to the letter.

Senator Flanders did see the work nearly completed but unfortunately he passed away a short time before the dedication.

To travel the seven miles to its new location, the roof of the bridge had to be removed for height clearance. Having leaked for years, the roof was no longer of any value. At the nearest unloading point it has been restored and is ready to go as soon as the new "River Bed" has been prepared.

The little Baltimore Bridge is being rolled over the brook that will come with the next rainstorm. The abutment stones were salvaged from the old setting.

Baltimore after the 1978 blizzard. Snow melting on roof. Windows were left open during restoration.

FLINT BRIDGE

TUNBRIDGE, VT.

This is the most northerly of five covered bridges on the First Branch of the White River. The road passing over this bridge leads to the Justin Morgan Farm where the Morgan Breed of horses "grew up".

Besides jacking to rebuild the ends and produce some cambre, it was necessary to install a totally new floor system and siding. The bridge was raised 2' to get good drainage and to make room to clean and cap the abutments. (See – The Last of the Covered Bridge Builders, Sharp Little Accessories.)

When we were working in 12° below 0 temperatures, the First Selectman visited us at the bridge. He said, "We have a complaint about the bridge being closed. Mary-Lou has to go a bit further to get to her bank job, but she is not complaining. However, as for Annabelle Lee, who is not pleased, I have little concern. She does not have to work and the sooner she gets home, the sooner she can hit the road again."

That the covered wooden bridge can be very ill and still work is evidenced by the following: I had made a casual appointment with engineers Frank Chase and Everett Perkins and also First Selectman Bowen to inspect the Flint Bridge. Two minutes after our arrival at the bridge, a partially loaded Mack milk truck passed through as he had daily for 20 years. The floor bent down several inches prompting

113

The bridge is thoroughly relaxed and the - cambre of 5" is changed to a + cambre of 8" before building in new ends.

Mr. Bowen to ask for an opinion. It was agreed by the engineers that closing the bridge that day would be none too soon. Mr. Bowen stated that until that year the town had used the bridge for crossing with their tandem road grader with snow plowing equipment.

Bridge floor being built. Son Arnold in foreground.

M. S. Graton & Arnold M. Graton   (Photo by Sean Callahan — LIFE Magazine)

N.E. COLLEGE BRIDGE

HENNIKER, N.H. — Built 1972

The campus of N.E. College is divided by the Contoocook River which runs from the extreme southern portion of New Hampshire to West Concord, where it joins the Merrimack.

Since there is but one bridge crossing the river in town, and that carrying a major route, there were times when traffic might have to await the pleasure of several hundred students. A direct line across the river from the gym to the developing athletic fields would save the students at least ½ mile of street travel each way.

In the early fall of 1970 a seminar was held at the College Library to which were invited officials and members of several covered bridge societies. Mr. & Mrs. Grant Musser, from the Cornell University town of Ithaca represented the New York State Covered Bridge Society. Mrs. Orrin Lincoln of Greenfield, Mass., the principal speaker, represented the Connecticut River Valley Covered Bridge Society, of which she is president. The National Society for the Preservation of Covered Bridges was also well represented.

It was the unanimous decision of the 100 people present that the bridging of the Contoocook River with an authentic covered bridge would serve the best interest of New England College.

During the fall we met several evenings with the Covered Bridge Committee and the Finance Committee. Since our work does not fall in a competitive field, we negotiated to place a 150' authentic covered bridge across the Contoocook River. Though the bridge was mainly for pedestrian travel it was to have a capacity of 15 tons to accommodate fire trucks and other necessary vehicles.

The bridge was to cost $72,000 plus $3,000 for the east abutment. The west abutment was to be built at cost because of the uncertainties. It was necessary to drive piling. The Corps of Engineers made available some old granite abutments for re-use to avoid the use of concrete.

This was, without question, the largest job that was done in New England that year without a performance bond and without a written agreement of any kind.

In March 1971 we were advised to go ahead with the work. We ordered the schedule of timber sawed in the State of Washington. This would provide for the trusses and floor timber. Work on the smaller components was started promptly at our shop from native timber.

When, on July 3, 1971, our carload of Douglas Fir finally arrived in Concord, N.H., after a three weeks delay in the Buffalo railroad yard, we trucked it to the site for drying.

At this time we had accumulated a back log of several house-moving jobs and Arnold had to be left alone to build the bridge with two new men in Henniker and David Howe, Jr. of Holderness who frames timber components at our shop.

Later in the fall of 1971 I was working alone in Henniker one Saturday. The Prof. of Engineering stopped by with his 12 year old son to whom I was introduced as the man who was building the covered bridge. The son was quick in responding. He said, "I have been here lots of times, but I never saw him here!" I felt like an unimportant part of the operation.

While the timber was drying, Arnold had time to lay up the two abutments of used granite from an old C.B. setting.

The young man seated on the end of the ramp is not meditating. He is checking the forward movement of the bridge. Those aboard are riding toll-free.

The New England College grounds department had prepared the subgrade for their road to the bridge and expanded it somewhat to provide us with a level spot where we could frame and erect the Towne Lattice trusses.

By Sept. 1st the moisture content had been reduced to 15% or a stabilized condition. We set up our planer to dress lightly both sides of the 4" x 12" and 4" x 14" timber as it was needed for assembly.

During September, October and November Arnold constructed the main trusses and erected them. He had also brought the pre-fitted roof trusses from our yard and completed the roof structure.

Now, that we were ready to shingle the roof, it started to snow some each day. It was quite hard to understand since the Old Farmer's Almanac, which is published 30 miles away and 90% right, had predicted fair weather. Finally a passing college student explained the unseasonable weather. The student body had been holding meetings to pray for good skiing conditions at "Pat's Peak."

By May 1 the roof and floor were finished and the bridge was ready to move forward to the west abutment.

I had been working in Ithaca on the Newfield Bridge and eventually got home for three weeks to help Arnold place the bridge across the Contoocook River. I then returned to New York while Arnold finished his bridge.

The Governor had, by proclamation, set aside the week of May 7 through May 14, 1972 as Covered Bridge Week in the State of New Hampshire. There was to be a dedication starting at 2 P.M. on Saturday the 13th with such speakers as Gov. Walter Peterson, Rep. Louis Wyman, College Pres. Jere Chase and representatives of various covered bridge societies, some from as far away as Ohio.

Gov. Walter Peterson and Milton Graton at New England College.

Owing to the fact that the oxen had spent two previous days moving the bridge part of the way across the river, for once we were on time. While the crowd, (conservatively estimated at 3,000) was watching the oxen move the bridge forward across the river, the gap was finally closed and at 1:30, the oxen, which had been so patient at their task were given some hay and allowed to mingle with the crowd and enjoy the dedication.

The two bridges above are 800' apart.

Arnold Graton visits owner Donald Crane at his Washington, N.H. saphouse to inspect oxen, Stars & Stripes. These oxen were candidates for moving the N.E. College covered bridge across the Contoocook River.

...bers of the football team. These athletes were candidates for the moving job — they lost.

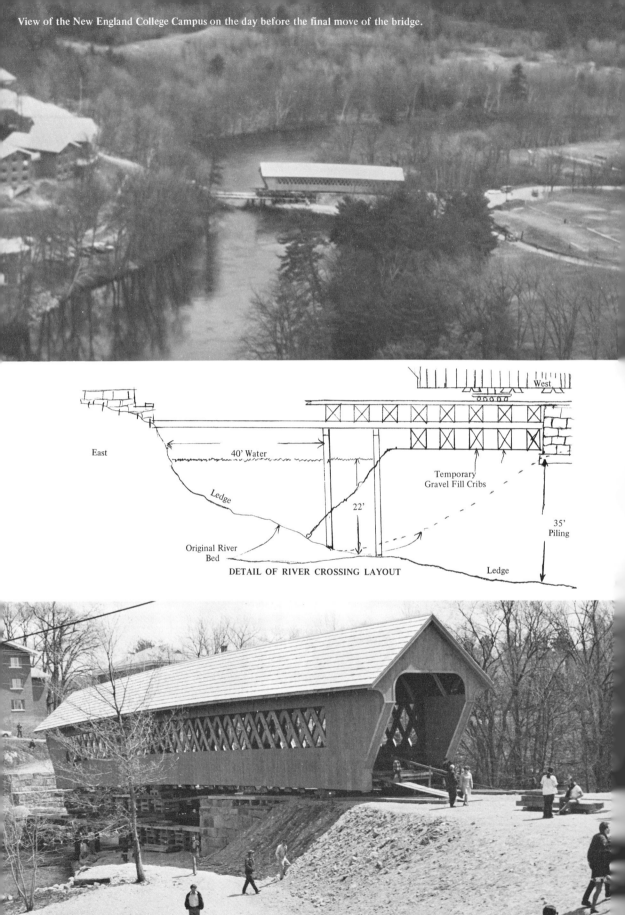

View of the New England College Campus on the day before the final move of the bridge.

West

East

40' Water

Ledge

Temporary
Gravel Fill Cribs

22'

35'
Piling

Original River
Bed

Ledge

DETAIL OF RIVER CROSSING LAYOUT

The Lincolns, 1976.   Photo by Dick Wilson

MR. & MRS. ORRIN LINCOLN

OF GREENFIELD, MASS.

The Lincolns have, without question, done more in the cause of saving our old covered bridges than any other two people in America.

As co-founders of the Connecticut River Valley Covered Bridge Society, they have worked tirelessly for over twenty-five years to create a better knowledge and appreciation of the old masterpieces of Americana.

Together with their society, they have always been found ready to aid financially in covered bridge preservation. Their great effort has been felt and appreciated throughout our country.

The above picture of the Lincolns was taken at the celebration of the twenty-fifth anniversary of the founding of the Connecticut River Valley Covered Bridge Society, of which Mrs. Lincoln is president.

NEWFIELD COVERED BRIDGE

NEWFIELD, N.Y.   BUILT IN 1853

What the bridge looked like when work was started on it.

This bridge is the only covered bridge remaining in Tompkins County. It was almost literally rescued from the burnable rubbish heap by the New York State Covered Bridge Society.

Mr. Graton and Thomas Howe drill hole in 12" x 16" timber; the holes are for rods which distribute the floor load between truss and assisting arch.

The arches set in shallow concrete channels are shown, in the abutments on the under side of the bridge.

Pictures and captions courtesy of Constructioneer Magazine, Chatham, New Jersey.

Straightening the Newfield Bridge.

The inside while installing arches.

The bridge re-built & raised 1 ft.

...he finished bridge with Mr. & Mrs. Musser who
...ere responsible for helping to save the bridge.
...he design on their clothes is of covered bridges.

The bridge was posted for three tons and was to be removed to make way for a modern bridge or a large pipe culvert as are found further down the stream. Since New York State has only twenty-three remaining covered bridges, the Society was very much disturbed and spent much time trying to convince the authorities to preserve this bridge. Their efforts finally paid off and I was invited to inspect the structure and advise as to the cost of restoration.

Commissioner Stevenson of the Tompkins County Dept. of Public Works had been convinced of the value of the old bridge! But how about his successor? Would there be another battle to try to convince him also twenty-five years hence and a chance to lose?

I decided that since I was now in the driver's seat we would design a repair that could, if the bridge was cared for, delay the next major confrontation for 100 years. Our negotiated price for restoration covered just that kind of repair job.

We recommended the things that we thought should be done. Our lump sum price was to be $44,000. There was no need to explain that we had been governed by the social as well as material matters. The County agreed to our proposal and we assumed responsibility for the bridge.

To protect ourselves and the County of Tompkins we shored up the bridge instead of closing it. Its condition was far from good. One truss was down 6", the other was down 8" and the top chord was buckled out 10". To prevent the top chords from buckling, when repaired 25 years earlier, four outriggers had been placed on each side.

Our list of cures was brief — we would perform the following services:

1. Create some cambre — as original.
2. Straighten top chord and repair.
3. Repair bottom chord where rotted.
4. Ream 2" trunnel holes to 2 1/8" and use 2 1/8" trunnels to eliminate elongated holes.
5. Raise cross ties from third chord to top chord.
6. Create new roof trusses and lateral braces to allow 26" more clearance.
7. Install a button system to hold down roof and secondary rafters to work with this system.
8. Eliminate outriggers.
9. Raise entire structure 1 foot for drainage.
10. Install an interceptor for water in front of portal on high side.
11. Install a pair of laminated arches with an end section of 12" x 32".
12. Shingle with ½" white cedar shingles 36" long.
13. Replace old clapboards with 1" x 8" dry hemlock, laid as clapboards.
14. Paint red as before.

Our working relationship with Commissioner Stevenson, County Engineer Mobbs, and other county people was unusually pleasant and agreeable. It is evident that they are glad to have made the right decision — to save.

To safeguard their only covered bridge, the County of Tompkins has created a county office, "Keeper of the Bridge". This is an honorary position and assures the bridge of the care it should have. The "Keeper" is expected to request attention for the bridge whenever he detects a need for it. The first appointed "Keeper" was the team of Mr. & Mrs. Grant Musser of Lansing, N.Y. The County had been asked to bend the rules and permit a keeper from outside Newfield because of the great effort of the Mussers in securing the preservation. Though Newfield Covered Bridge is the only one known to be so protected it is a move in the right direction.

REPLACING BUMP BRIDGE

      The Campton Board of Selectmen were anxious to see what could be done to the Bump Bridge "to keep it going for a few more years". We recalled, from our experience years before, that our working experience had been pleasant, that they had been exacting in their dealings and mindful of their financial commitments.

Old Bump Bridge, Built 1877, Removed 1972

I agreed with the Selectmen that, based upon that which could be seen, we would be willing to repair the bridge for $2,500. We propped it up for the winter and were surprised in early spring to hear from the road agent that it had fallen apart and he had closed the bridge.

Upon cleaning out the trusses, we found all bottom framing areas to be completely rotted. There was nothing to repair. How could the Town Fathers explain the sudden change from bridge to no bridge?

Since the Town of Campton had Blair, a larger bridge, in need of restoration and had an estimate from the State Engineers on the cost if the State did the work, I suggested to the Selectmen, "Let's Make a Deal!"

1. If the Town of Campton would put the larger bridge job up for competitive bidding, I would submit a bid which would be within the engineers' estimate.
2. I would build a new 68' covered bridge with a capacity of 10 tons and an estimated cost of $14,000 for the agreed repair price of $2,500.
3. I would borrow $10,000 to do the job and trust that my wages plus any profit on the large bridge job would be enough to help repay the bank loan.

I borrowed $10,000, completed the new bridge and upon receipt of a check for $2,500 this part of our "deal" was closed.

The Campton Selectmen and I learned later that owing to the type of work to be done there was no qualified competitive bidder for the Blair Bridge. After calling for bids it might be considered discriminatory to reject the bids on negative grounds. Three years later, after much red tape and paper work, we did the restoration of Blair for the Town of Campton on an hourly basis. The State then reimbursed the Town.

Replacement for Bump Bridge, Built 1972, Length 66'

Blenheim Covered Bridge over Schoharie Creek in N. Blenheim, N.Y.

    Although this great bridge spans a river that is usually 100' or less in width, a brief rain will cause the river to reach from one abutment to the other. At the right in the above picture is a dry portion of river bed that is 80' wide and used in flood periods.

    To avoid restricting the waterway by filling to the main bridge, it seems to have been decided that a less professionally built covered bridge would do for the very short span. We are told that this did not last many years and was replaced with an iron bridge shown at the right. This in turn was broken down by a passing threshing machine prior to 1933.

BLENHEIM BRIDGE

    The Blenheim Covered Bridge over Schoharie Creek in N. Blenheim, N.Y. is the longest single span covered bridge in the world. This 228', double barrel bridge was built in 1854 by Nicholas Powers who lived near Rutland, Vermont.

    That which one could see of the bridge, through the bushes, looked O.K. However, it was feared by some that a check-up might be in order. We were invited to inspect the bridge and did so a few months later. Meeting with Robert Schaffer, Blenheim's Town Supervisor, and noting his admiration for the bridge and also his determination to see that it was kept in good condition, it was at once apparent that others in responsible positions did not share his thoughts. The poor old bridge was putting on a good show. It was suffering from "Covered Bridge Arthritis" at all bearing areas.

    At the southwest end of the bridge, a grading job had been done to create a picnic area. A light berm had been built to keep the water from flowing toward the bridge, but visitors had worn a path through the berm and for years the water had run into the abutment and the bedding timbers.

    Timbers which were once 10" thick had decomposed to a thickness of 4 or 5" plus a bit of garden material. The great arches (of three layers of 10 x 10) were of pine above the floor level, but of white oak from the floor to the granite abutments where pine might rot due to dampness. The ends of the arches had rotted less than the corner timbers, but they could not avoid the extra tons of weight transferred to them. Being well contained, the arches pushed the blocks of dry granite back into the abutments and absorbed the balance of the movement by crumbling at the ends.

At the opposite end of the bridge there was not enough dampness to promote rapid decay so, as if to assure this, someone had poured concrete around the bed timbers 20 years earlier. That was all it needed.

We negotiated a series of little agreements in 1972-73 to correct the various ills.

Since all four corners were rotted some, the Blenheim Bridge could not be expected to rest on a series of short splices. To replace the members of the bottom chords, with original splices at 10, 20, 30 & 40 feet from the bridge ends would require jacking positions 50' from the bridge ends. This would cost much money and Mr. Schaffer, the Town Supervisor, was all but begging for the bridge funds which he did secure.

I decided that the only way to secure a long term repair would be to make the necessary short splices and carry a 3' x 3' reinforced concrete bar out from the abutment far enough to provide support for the second set of vertical posts. The timber in this area had not been unduly exposed to moisture and was sound.

We plug drilled and split the granite of the abutments removing enough granite to allow the concrete bar to reach under the first vertical posts.

We constructed thrust blocks for the great arch in the center truss which provided support for the truss also. After the vertical supports had been raised about eight inches, the arch was then placed under more than thirty tons pressure and made secure.

The bridge is now in fairly good physical condition. We would like to have done more, but time is always in short supply and must be allocated where needed most.

(Photo by Edmund Homer Royce from The Covered Bridge by Herbert Wheaton Congdon)
According to the Waitsfield Historical Society this picture of the Village Bridge was taken about 1918 before it had faced many years of neglect.

BRIDGES AT WAITSFIELD, VT.

VILLAGE BRIDGE – 1834
Second Oldest Covered Bridge in Vermont

The Waitsfield bridges are not of great importance because of their size. Their claim-to-fame rests in their will and determination to exist! They have had as difficult a life as one could possibly imagine.

Like many small towns, but 7½ times worse than most, Waitsfield has its "Hatfields and McCoys". The Hatfields, supported by the local historical society, were determined to save the town's covered bridges. The McCoys were equally determined to destroy, to make room for modern bridges.

(Photo by Edmund Homer Royce from The Covered Bridge by Herbert Wheaton Congdon)
The sidewalk was added about 1940. When we started to work the sidewalk was hanging from the bridge and part had fallen into the water. It sagged 6" at the middle and had to be hauled 13" to the south to make it erect again.

Pine Brook West Portal.

Pine Brook East Portal after rebuilding and raising one and one half feet.

Pine Brook East Portal. Though no repairs had been done for many years, the bridge was open to traffic when we arrived for work. These portal decorations are said to have been displayed off and on for three years of the last four to discredit the bridge.

Pine Brook. North side showing posts in the brook. This side sags more than is apparent. The corner nearest the camera was rotten and settled 8".

In the case of the Village Bridge, the 6" laminated floor had basins 3 to 4" deep rotted in the traveled surface and never filled with cold patch. They were usually, therefore, filled with water in wet weather and trucks would pound through them. It was so shamefully neglected that there are no pictures of that era available.

Though the towns people voted for our negotiated offer to restore the bridge and the State approved it, nothing was done and nearly a year later the State took it over. In the process of trying to produce a proposal that was "bidable" the State had to include some steel "knee braces". However, when we started work the State Engineers were very considerate in allowing us to substitute wooden "ship knees" for the steel.

Now about four years after our restoration, the Village Bridge has been placed on the National Register for protection and the towns people have decided to close it to the use of 12 cu. yd. loaded gravel trucks. These trucks had used it at will.

PINE BROOK BRIDGE — 1870

Pine Brook was placed on the Historic Register some time ago. This entitles the town to Federal Aid equal to ½ the cost of restoration or repair.

The town government had been given two heavy I beams on which they planned to pour a concrete deck and then set the crippled bridge on that as is. The Historic Sites Commission would not pass this as an "historic preservation" and they would not contribute their promised $7,000. Next, we are told, there was a try at using a timber deck as a perch for the old bridge. This didn't qualify as historic either.

We were under some pressure from those who wanted to save the bridge to devise some way of that being done. Since there was only $14,000 available, it was a case of doing a job that ultimately cost us $18,000, for the available money or seeing it destroyed for lack of funding. This would be the sure-fire way out for the destroyers!

I agreed that we would submit a "bid" of $14,000 to save the bridge provided the I beams be merely STORED under the bridge and at an elevation which would lack ½" of making any physical contact with the bridge. There would be no assistance from the steel unless a heavily loaded "outlaw" came along. In that case the bridge deck timber would spring down, make contact and spring back to its initial position.

Upon our last trip to do a few odd touch-ups we noted that a gravel pit had been opened near the west end of the bridge and 12 cu. yd. loads of gravel were passing through the little 8 ton bridge. This has since been remedied, we are told, as in the case of their other bridge.

Conclusion:

We have spent some of our own money there, paid for travel distance of the school bus, avoided payment of a threatened three thousand dollar late fine, saved two nice old covered bridges, left town without being shot at and left the "Hatfields and McCoys" to fight it out.

DOWNER'S BRIDGE

WEATHERSFIELD, VERMONT — BUILT ABOUT 1870

This bridge was once one of the most tidily built bridges in Vermont. From the splendid, well laid, stone approach walls and abutments to the portal finish with splined boarding, it was outstanding.

Filling the approaches over the years had left the bridge floor as the lowest place and water running into the bridge had caused much rot.

We rebuilt the trusses and raised the bridge 2½' for drainage and also built new backwalls. We re-framed the floor system with heavier joists. Time would not permit of our doing more so others covered the floor and south side.

The Bicentennial Edition of the publication "American Wooden Bridges" by the American Society of Civil Engineers, features on its cover, the opposite portal of this bridge.

Photo taken at flood crest, March 19, 1936, thirty-seven feet above low water mark. Insert, near normal level thirty days later.

BEDELL COVERED BRIDGE

HAVERHILL, N.H. TO NEWBURY, VT.

This bridge is, in our opinion, the outstanding example of long span timber truss bridging. It was built in 1866 and has a total length of 396' in 2 spans. The type of truss used is Double Burr Arch. It had, for many years, been an important link in this main line from Concord, N.H. to Montpelier, Vermont crossing the Connecticut River.

I will touch very lightly on this bridge, not because it deserves that treatment but because it is a very complex matter through its 110 year life. It would require a book to cover the construction and the great floods it has taken in stride; the abuse from leaking roof to the entrance of water on the floor from poor road drainage on the Vt. end.

Laminated arches.

Using 4 grip hoists of 1½ ton capacity which were used with 4 to 6 snatch blocks each, we shortened the bottom chord after the weight was off the truss.

The bottom chords were allowed to become rotten and were patched around the period of the 1927 flood. At this time laminated arches were installed to add to the strength, and the carpentry was good — but the ends were embedded in concrete for some six inches and in a short time accumulated dampness and rotted off. For years these arches have been a burden instead of a help.

The 1927 flood put water into the bridge to a height of 5 feet but the bridge was fastened down to the abutments by use of heavy rods. This apparently kept the bridge from floating away.

In 1973 there was a July flood which nearly finished this bridge. There had been an effort, over a 10 year period, to get an appropriation to restore the bridge but each time something unfavorable happened. After the flood the Bedell Bridge became worse. Near the center pier one truss broke and dropped 31" in 24 feet. Nineteen inches of drop or sag was not uncommon in many places.

Laminated arches where rotted.

After the laminated arches had rotted off and the end containment of the Burr Arch had failed, many of the vertical posts broke off as above.

The towns of Newbury, Vt. and Haverhill, N.H. had deeded their ownership in the bridge to the State of New Hampshire with the condition that the State restore it. Now, the State, out of fear of the bridge floating down stream and causing damage, had let a contract to wreck the bridge. When news of this action reached the people on both banks of the Connecticut River, many were more than concerned for their bridge.

Gov. Meldrim Thomson of N.H. was invited to a meeting of several hundred Vt. and N.H. people in Woodsville, N.H. He brought with him several engineers to support the theory that the bridge could not be saved. We are told that all was not pleasant at that meeting. The State granted a group of interested people 5 days to furnish a $1,000,000 guarantee against damage and evidence that they were financially responsible for doing the job of restoration. This group became Bedell Bridge Incorporated (non-profit), and chose Mr. Stephen Wellington, a Haverhill resident, as president.

We were contacted for an opinion. We could only use the stock answer, "Nothing is impossible." We signed an agreement for restoration "Not to exceed $200,000." This amount seemed like a lot of money. But Bedell was the second longest two-span covered bridge in the United States and we knew there was never as sick a one that stayed out of the river! It had to be the biggest repair job in Covered Bridge history and if it stumped us, no one would want it. The bridge was of such a "touch & go" nature that Mr. Wellington said to my son Arnold, "Don't worry about going to work on it. Even if it falls into the river we will pay you for whatever work you have done." No thought was given to where **we** would be found to accept payment.

We changed the bridge, temporarily to a suspension by using two ribbons of five — 1½" wires each. The worst span (N.H.) is now back on line and grade within an inch. At the center pier it was raised 15" plus rot and settlement and on the N.H. end it was raised 2 feet and 3 feet. The rotted arch ends have been opened up, some as much as 30 feet. New leaves have been inserted and the arches are again at work. The project is to be completed in Nov. 1978.

The Bedell Bridge was completely restored and turned over to the State of New Hampshire in July, 1979.

The five — 1½" wires used to make the Bedell a suspension.

The Bedell as a suspension bridge.

N.H. span back on line & grade.

Raising the bridge. Left, Arnold Graton, Jr., 1974.

When jacking was completed on N.H. span in 1974, the arches were cut off to eliminate rot. New thrust pads were cast at ends.

To saw off the old arches, Arnold is standing at old ground level. We excavated by hand under the granite and poured 34 c.y. of concrete for a footing.

The January, 1978 thaw caused an ice jam at Bedell and for more than a mile in either direction. The depth at shore was 4 to 8'. Two feet of good hard ice formed in the top of this jam and we decided to jack the bridge from it. The jacking posts were suspended by a chain which was passed through a hole in the end of the timber. Apprentices: Jeffrey Baker, Stanley Graton 2nd, Arnold Graton, Jr.

The Vermont Span of Bedell still lacks 8" of being raised level at the center. During the 1927 repair, this span was down 12" and the bottom chord was made longer by fitting in new members tightly at ends where previous members had slipped.

The river varied in height as much as 15" as "peak" loads effected the discharge at the power station up stream. When the river was going down slowly was the best time to jack. If we jacked too slowly the jack would go down and leave the post hanging. To jack when the river could help you was unsafe as you might get the jacks stuck and get **too much** help.

BLAIR COVERED BRIDGE

BUILT 1868-69

The fact that our covered bridges should be preserved is evident by the fact that within two years of our restoration of the Blair Covered Bridge, this fine restaurant sprang up beside it.

It is recorded that prior to 1828 there had been a fording place in the Pemigewasset River near the present location of Blair Bridge. During a storm the local doctor lost his horse while fording the river on horseback. The town voted in 1828 to build a covered bridge at the present bridge location. The fact that this bridge was completely burned by an arsonist in 1868 seems to have been overlooked in publications. The Campton Town History, however, states very clearly that the arsonist, at his trial for the crime, claimed that the Lord had commanded him to burn the bridge.

The present bridge was built in 1868 and in rebuilding it we found only one timber remaining of the 1828 bridge. At the center pier there is a 12" x 16" timber, which is 20 feet long and sound, though it is charred on all sides. We must conclude that this member was employed as a cross sill on the pier and when the burning bridge fell into the river, this sill was left "high and dry" without enough to finish its destruction. It is still carrying its load.

The Blair Bridge is very important on the list of "musts" in the saving of our covered bridges. There are several reasons: Blair is the last covered bridge remaining on the Merrimack-Pemigewasset River system. It is the longest two span covered bridge in New Hampshire. Its length is 300 feet although some publications list it as 273 feet long. As a long span bridge it is constructed of unusually light timbers and has resisted sagging very well. The granite abutments were well built and although they are cracked from the intense heat of the burning bridge in 1868, they will stand for a long time yet.

In 1977 we completely rebuilt the four corners of this bridge. This was necessary due to decay caused by dirt and dampness. We also raised the east end of the bridge 8 inches and nearly all the floor joists were replaced in the laying of the new 4 inch plank floor. Oak plank were used in the truck-travel pattern.

The Blair Covered Bridge should be placed on the National Historic Register.

This heavily loaded "ten-wheeler", on a Saturday afternoon shortcut, 20 years ago, nearly made it over 300 ft. long Blair. Though the bridge was posted for 6 ton limit this loaded truck is estimated to have exceeded 16 tons. The truck belonged to the Draper Corp. now Rockwell International. Photo loaned by Elmer Tobine.

Blair Covered Bridge — built in 1868 to replace one burned by arsonist a year before. (M.S. Graton) Photo, Oct. 1975, courtesy of Harlen Persinger of the Webb Co. (Publishers) St. Paul, Minn.

East end of Blair Covered Bridge while new bottom chords and vertical post splices were installed. Traffic was carried on a short bridge within a bridge!

The abutment cracked by fire 100 years ago, was drilled and doweled to receive reinforced concrete frame. This is carried forward under the chords to support the second verticals from the end.

Dressing floor plank for thickness with portable planer. Arnold feeding part of old floor material in background.

Moving joists into Blair Bridge after trimming. L. Torsey with "dolly", Arnold Graton trimming.

Blair Bridge – typical corner repair, 1977.

East portal after completion. A small piece of board found still nailed to the west end indicated arched ends existed years ago.

Blair Bridge during high water, 1977. Photo by M.S. Graton

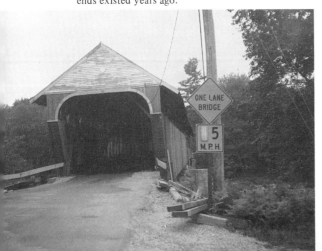

CLOSING

There is a great difference between a job that is done for the sole purpose of accumulating financial wealth and that done for the purpose of preserving.

On the one hand, if the person doing the work does not like the pay received he can go on a strike and quit work or even more, he can prevent others from working by using picket lines. He usually gets his wishes satisfied or the total effort comes to a halt.

On the other hand, one who sympathizes with those who would save the old or the valuable can only ask a modest sum for his services. Money comes hard, very hard, for those public-spirited folks who try to bridge the gap between the bridge and the preservers.

To say that one is respectful of yesterday's men and the products of their toils, but to admit that his feeling goes only as far as the dollar will carry it, exposes his basic character. However, one can carry on the rebuilding of some unfortunate and neglected bridge to the end, to find that he has spent the available money, consumed that of his family and must ask his materials suppliers to await the possible understanding of his bank.

As of today, the good printers at Clifford-Nicol toil painstakingly in an effort to create, on paper, a conveyance for certain illustrations and thoughts to be carried forward to posterity. It is hoped that this work will complement the structures which we have tried to pass on.

The great Bedell Bridge is due to be completed this fall and other tentative commitments will have to be deferred for the time.

We have, this week, signed a modest little agreement with the Frankenmuth Bavarian Inn of Frankenmuth, Michigan for a covered bridge to be built across the Cass River. The 240' bridge will have a traveled way 19' wide to accommodate two way passenger car traffic to a 350 car parking lot.

Trailways Busses and the like will use the bridge as one lane.

May you have pleasant crossings.

Most sincerely,

Milton S. Graton

147

Zehnder's Holz-Brücke ready to be dressed.   Photo by Glenn Baker of Frankenmuth, Michigan

Placing roof trusses and rafters.   Photo by Frankenmuth News

THE BUILDING
of
ZEHNDER'S
HOLZ-BRÜCKE

19 ZEHNDER'S 79
HOLZ BRÜCKE
(WOODEN BRIDGE)
Frankenmuth, Michigan

M. S. Graton, Bill Zehnder and A. M. Graton. Bridge move completed.　　　Photo by Glenn Baker of Frankenmuth.

The completed end of the Zehnder's Holz-Brücke.   Photo by Geraldine Reed

DEFINITION OF AUTHENTIC HIGHWAY COVERED BRIDGE

The authentic highway covered bridge, as we see it, being America's only designers and erectors today, should meet the following requirements:

All materials for the structure should originate in the forest from replaceable sources, (replaceable in kind but not necessarily in quality). The kind of tree or timber will grow again with the setting out of new forests. That is all that man can do to replace in kind and it is a very commendable effort, but in our modern world the quality of this first cutting may never be achieved. These large timbers, some 6" x 16" x 32' long, which are select structural in grade with only very small knots, can only be produced from trees one to two hundred years old. No one will pay taxes on the second one hundred years of the tree life. During this period the semi-mature tree slows down its rapid growth while creating choice quality timber. This quality timber can be produced only in that portion of the tree's life cycle.

The framing positons should be created through conventional joining and not by the introduction of "labor saving" steel gadgets or fittings, which bypass the skilled framer. The "back bone" or frame of the bridge should be composed of a

truss on either side. The covered bridge which is built on stringers has no real need for a cover because there is no framing to catch the moisture of rains which causes decay. I have heard of one young man of the "covered bridge variety" describe this construction as "Mickey-Mouse", by which he meant pure pretense. If, in early days, a bridge were to be supported on stringers in long lengths, these stringers would be alternated as to tips and butts.

They would not be hewed to the size permitted by the size of the tip end. Should a tree be found that would hew out a sixty foot timber of uniform size, this timber would, of course, not sustain its own weight to say nothing of the dead weight of the structure of which it was to be a part. With this reasoning in mind, we can see the justification for Caesar's reported pride in describing his bridging of the Rhine River with many short spans. We do not find clear or descriptive records of Ario-vistus' means of crossing rivers, but being on the defensive, he might have been forced to use a primitive way which might not become the dignity of the Tenth Legion.

Though there are many recognized types of truss and variations of them, their respectability varies with the quantity of iron rods and other metal parts involved.

The roofing of the covered bridge comes in for much explaining as to reason. Some oft-written reasons are as follows:

1. To comfort an otherwise frightened horse with the thought that he was entering a barn.
2. To shelter travelers from the rain.
3. To allow one to hide with his neighbor's girlfriend or daughter.
4. To shelter a farmer's load of hay in a shower.

But the one overpowering reason for the bridge being covered is to prevent such damage as would come to your house if it had a leaking roof. The first four reasons mentioned, though no doubt welcome, must be considered to be by-products.

Why a covered bridge today when the country-side is literally "flooded" with steel and concrete structures? First of all, it costs no more, we are told, to create a 12 to 15 ton capacity covered bridge than a modern one of steel and concrete. The expected useful life of a covered bridge, with reasonable care, would be upward of 100 years. (The youngest covered bridge that we have restored is over 100 years old and the oldest is 146.) These, when restored, are good for another 100 years. The covered bridge brings back an appreciation of the mellowness of yesterday's skills as compared with the severity of today's mechanical monsters. In the climate where snow and slippery roads require the use of road salt, a modern concrete deck has a life expectancy of 25 to 30 years. Since we have witnessed the use of salt for slightly over forty years and the deck replacements only once, the cost of the second deck replacement can not be calculated from actual experience! The covered bridge, on the other hand, has no snow on the deck to require salting and the deck has no cause for concern even if salt were used. The maintenance of the covered bridge consists of blowing the deck and lower chords clean annually and keeping the roof tight. The use of an air compressor for a period of one half day each year with a restricted discharge on the compressed air line will thoroughly clean the average covered bridge. One might say that the concrete and steel bridge is not seen to be requiring any maintenance. If such cleaning, washing, sand blasting, and painting is not being done, it follows that "cancer" is surely developing and major repairs are inevitable.

THE FRANKENMUTH BRIDGE

In the summer of 1972 we received a letter from the Frankenmuth Bavarian Inn stating that they might be interested in purchasing a covered bridge and that they would like to talk with us if we could come from New Hampshire to Frankenmuth, Michigan for conference. Since we always have three or four years work scheduled or at least waiting, we await a second invitation before visiting, especially at 1,000 miles distance.

In September 1973, while visiting in Phoenix, Arizona, I wrote to Tiny Zehnder to determine if the Frankenmuth Bavarian Inn was still interested in talking. In returning to New Hampshire we could visit our daughter and family near Chicago or return via Frankenmuth, Michigan. We were advised that a visit would be appreciated and we responded a few days later. We arrived late on a Sunday afternoon. Yes, the usual lines were drawn up in battle formation. My wife suggested that we park our travel trailer and return to the inn. This we did and found what appeared to be the same lines still formed. Finally, we were escorted by Tiny Zehnder behind the lines for our "reservation" and arrangements were made for a 10 a.m. meeting.

Eight o'clock next morning found us looking over the town of Frankenmuth. We were most favorably impressed. You might ask what relationship exists between the town and the building of a covered bridge. Since the building of a covered bridge or the restoration of one is not a commercial venture and you are going to be giving of your limited time to create something to be left in town, it would be satisfying to know that there would be appreciation. This appreciation would be best expressed in the care given the bridge. Since good housekeeping can safely be considered contagious on a municipal scale as well as on a domestic one, when we met Mr. Zehnder at 10 a.m., we had been convinced that what we had seen was not "window dressing".

Tiny Zehnder escorted us across the street to meet his brother, Eddie. Upon entering Zehnder's, we were introduced to Eddie's wife as covered bridge builders from New Hampshire. Mrs. Eddie Zehnder lost no time in asking, "Tiny, are you still thinking of that?" Tiny confessed that he was. Later we learned that the Zehnder Brothers had been dwelling on this scheme for 10 years and it was evident that they had worn a thin spot in that virtue known as patience. We spent the day at the Cass River location for the proposed covered bridge, obtaining soundings and elevations. The Zehnders asked that we return with a sketch indicating the size of a proposed covered bridge, the waterway and location, for a presentation to the United States Army Corps of Engineers.

To point out the difference between the planning for a covered bridge and a conventional bridge, I would like to cite an instance. When I reached New Hampshire I wrote to my old friend Colonel Wilbar Hoxie, a 35 year veteran of the Corps of Engineers at Waltham, Massachusetts. I told him of our visit to Frankenmuth and the approximate location of the proposed covered bridge. Before there was time for the Corps Headquarters at Detroit to mail me the information I had requested from them, Colonel Hoxie had obtained all available Corps information and had it in my hands! He offered further service if desired and stated that his special interest in this covered bridge stemmed from the fact that Governor Cass, Michigan's first governor, was one of his ancestors. The data, the Colonel sent to me, was complete records of borings, dikes and sump pumps.

We returned to Frankenmuth, Michigan early in the winter to meet the Corps of Engineers, State Highway Engineers, Town Officials and numerous other interested parties. Our presentation consisted of 150 selected slides of restorations of old covered bridges and the building of new ones. The meeting was very pleasant as a memory and there were none of the road blocks that are usually presented. The Corps, on the other hand, granting that if a covered bridge were to be built in Michigan, Frankenmuth would be the ideal place for one.

A month later we received a letter from the Corps, one suitable for display framing, stating in essence that their delegation felt more enlightened on leaving than upon arrival. Though we had provided for a waterway under our proposed covered bridge which was equal to that of a State bridge on Main Street, we would have to increase our waterway. The reason for this being that the state built a waterway for the 25 or 50 year storm while the Corps of Engineers builds for or to accommodate the 100 year storm.

Though we responded to other invitations to Frankenmuth meetings, the project remained on the back burner for several years. Finally, in the winter of 1978 we were told that the Zehnders might be ready to "Go" and to show up with something consistent with the present lumber market.

Our lumber supplier could find but one mill on the West Coast which would agree to saw a schedule of timber for a covered bridge at this time and they would require ninety days for production. Acceptance of their quotation was good for thirty days only. On this visit to Frankenmuth, Michigan, we discussed a few remaining matters and left with the assurance, "You will hear from us".

After three weeks, we received a telephone call from Tiny Zehnder as follows, "They tell me that our thirty-day lumber quotation is about to expire. Assume that we have an agreement and place the special order. Get something to us".

We immediately placed the order which consisted in part as follows:

Douglas Fir — Select Structural:

125 pieces of 4 x 12 - 24' long	64 pieces of 6 x 16 - 32' long
125 pieces of 4 x 14 - 24' long	64 pieces of 6 x 16 - 20' long
64 pieces of 4 x 12 - 32' long	30 pieces of 10 x 12 - 34' long
64 pieces of 4 x 14 - 32' long	

There were required other woods.

Sawed locally:

Cedar shingles - ½" thick, 3' long boards from 70 cords of logs in lengths of 9' 4".

Spruce plank - 320 pieces of 4 x 8 - 16' long.

The first order amounted to three rail car loads of lumber.

We sent what I considered to be the seeds for a "Zehnder-created" agreement. Three days later my document was returned. The Zehnders had signed it and sent this letter: "Please sign this and have it notarized and return it. We will have copies made for distribution." This was Zehnders' idea of an old-fashioned, iron-clad covered bridge building contract. There were no plans, no specifications, and no performance bond. Our simple agreement did mention the bearings, to be built by others, and their several measurements. It also noted that the bridge would, in our

The first rail car of timber arrives at Gera.
Photo by Doris Graton

Picking off small bites with timber lift.
Photo by Doris Graton

iking timber off trailer with farm tractor and "sticking up".

Short 6" x 16" floor joists being "stuck up" and made ready for covering.

Photos by Doris Grāton

Long floor joists, 6" x 16" x 32' long, are being covered.

judgement, have a 15 ton capacity. We are told that the contract plans and specifications for the grading of the parking lot and providing of abutments, consumed upwards of fifty pages. One might wonder how much things have become streamlined in the past 100 years.

In July 1978 the first of the three rail cars carrying a total of 100,000 board feet of lumber arrived from Oregon. During the following month, the other two loads also reached Gera, about six miles from Frankenmuth. The timber was unloaded at the Gera railroad yard and trucked to the bridge location, where it was air dried. This lumber was carefully stuck up, the timber ends sprayed with several applications of Diesel fuel and battened down tightly with 6 millimeter polyethylene. This black covering would raise the temperature but not allow a too rapid loss of surface moisture from the timber; thus preventing season checking. A fourth car load was shipped directly to our Ashland, New Hampshire plant where it was to be framed into the upper bridge assemblies.

It was about this time that we started to discover what makes the City of Frankenmuth and the surrounding countryside CLICK! We needed white cedar shingles composed of ½" thick boards in three foot lengths. After searching the Upper Peninsula of Michigan, we finally found a swamp west of Alpena which had a substantial growth of white cedar. We arranged for this to be cut and delivered to the outskirts of Frankenmuth where Winnie Kern, a retired millwright, and Oscar Huber, a retired insurance broker, went to work on the necessary 130 squares of shingles. These two men and their helpers also sawed the 4 x 8 spruce plank for the deck.

155

Being 1,000 miles from our base of supply, we were often out of something, but some good neighbor would not fail to respond. All seemed anxious to be a part of what they considered their town's project.

During the early spring of 1979 we moved in several trailer loads of equipment, consisting of timber and prefitted upper bridge components.

Before laying out the work for building the bridge, we had determined the center line of the abutments and had projected that line up the grade and over into the leveled work area which was built on the parking lot. From this base line all of our layout work was carried on. The bedding timbers were arranged so that when a side truss was clamped together (400 complete clamps per side) and tipped up into an erect position, it stood accurately on the line to its final position.

Arnold trimming first 4" x 14" x 32' bottom chord members. Other timber is temporary falsework.
Photo by Doris Graton

About the middle of May, Arnold, my oldest son, with a helper, started to lay out the south side truss. This truss was 240' long and 20' high when stood up. It contained over thirty thousand board feet of lumber. By late June, we had erected the first truss. Our crew sometimes had a day or two when a visiting covered bridge "Buff" would lend a hand. This would suddenly swell our crew to five, but it was more often three or four workers. One young man, a true covered bridge "Buff", who was known to many visitors as "John, the pilot", has left his flying job in Vermont on several one-week periods to assist in the driving of trunnels and hand-raising of trusses.

156

TRUNNELS AND TIMBERS

The trunnels are 2" diameter white oak pins which are turned round except for a ¾" square portion at one end. This square top fits into a driving cap. These average to drive one inch with each blow of a 16 pound hammer. The trunnels in this bridge are 11", 24", and 27½" long for different locations in the chords and lattice. We had a total of 2,400 pieces of square stock, which were turned into trunnels.

In the Town Lattice type of truss, such as the Frankenmuth bridge, the trunnels and timbers must live in harmony to be successful. Since the intersecting areas of the timbers are pinned together in a fashion that causes the dimension of the unchanging timber to be made fast to the timber with a changing dimension, we planned ahead to insure that the timber with the changing dimension was stabilized. To do this the timbers had to be reduced to a moisture content of 14 to 15%, which is the reading that we would expect to find prevalent in the average covered bridge climate five years hence.

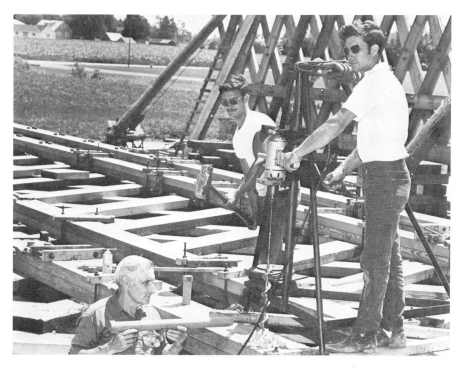

Milton Grāton, son Arnold, grandson Arnold Jr. placing trunnels.   Photo by Glenn Baker

Timber behavior can be likened to that of man. Man can get fat if provided with a barrel of chocolates. He will not grow taller. We must get man worked down through exercise and feed him Quaker Oats, as we might a horse. In this way we can be sure of his behavior. In the other dimension, (height) man is not subject to sudden changes. Timber likewise has no measureable changes in length.

As the timber is stabilized, so also is the size of the hole that is drilled in the stabilized wood. The trunnels were created of timber that was also stabilized. To be of wood that is over dried would be to create internal stresses in the framing timber when moisture was reabsorbed. To have a moisture content above 14 to 15%, would mean a loose-fitting trunnel when stabilized; and perhaps sagging trusses.

In the building of the Zehnder's Holz-Brücke, we had only a year to prepare the trunnels. Our stock of stabilized timber would yield only one third of this dimension. White oak is very slow to give up its moisture. The accepted rule for air drying oak is one year for each inch of thickness, or in this case, two and one-third years. To force-dry oak for turning would mean many season checks in the wood and a trunnel head that would fall apart in driving. To overcome this we sawed the squares of trunnel stock 2½" and stuck them up with ½" x ½" stickers. We applied a coat of linseed oil to the ends each second day for five applications. When the outdoor drying season was finished, we restuck the material in our home basement. The material was arranged so that warm air was blown the entire thirty foot length, under the six foot high pile, which was twenty-eight inches in the third dimension. This pile was then covered tightly with polyethylene to contain nearly all the expelled moisture. The heating process was carried on for 12 weeks. We generally heated for 2 hours before our working day, 2 hours after work, and 2 hours in late evening. The heat-off hours permitted equalization of moisture in the oak squares. Some may say that all of this "Old Maid" treatment is unnecessary, but there is a great difference between a good piece of trunnel stock and a stick of fireplace wood.

As the side trusses were laid out and clamped in a curve (14" of cambre), more than 400 complete clamps were employed. Before drilling each cluster of three holes, a short piece of lattice stock was jacked tightly under the hole location to prevent the wood from flaking away when the drill broke through at the bottom

The second truss being raised by manpower.

Photo by Glenn Baker

158

of a hole. More than one-half mile of holes were drilled in this bridge. In the driving of the trunnels a jack was placed under the timber nearby to prevent recoil of the chord, and to increase the net penetration. A penetration of 1" per blow from a 16 pound hammer is considered ideal, so in 24" of timber 18 blows would indicate too loose a fit, and on the other hand, 30 blows would be too tight. In this case of misfit, a slightly larger or smaller auger must be used.

The second truss laid out.   Photo by Glenn Baker

When the first side truss had been completely pinned together, the erecting was done by man power. To assure that the truss did not bend in the raising process, it was necessary to shim the bottom chord at numerous points to compensate for the amount of cambre that had been produced at each point. This would maintain a straight line through the hinging points and prevent premature stresses. In erecting the side, seven jacking positions were prepared and jacks placed under the third chord. At these positions, the structure was jacked about six feet, as far as jacking would permit.

From this position to that of an erect truss, the raising was done with ginpoles. The ginpole was stood so as to lean slightly toward the truss, and a lifting yoke made secure around the ginpole. The wire rope that was to do the lifting was secured to the top of the ginpole, then passed through a snatch block at the lifting yoke and returned to another

Lining up floor stiffeners.   Photo by Glenn Baker

Threading floor joists through second truss. Truss was moving

Photo by Glenn Baker

block at the top of the ginpole and finally back to the puller at the ginpole base. Each of the seven ginpoles was equipped in the same manner and the side was ready to raise. Four or five men can raise the side in this manner in one day. The second truss was built and raised by the same method as the first.

After the sides had been raised it was necessary, when a sidewalk is involved, to thread the floor joists through one truss above the bottom chord. The joists are alternated, short and long, so that every four feet there is a joist projecting far enough to support the walk and the long roof over-hang. The second truss was then rolled sidewise into its final position with the unsized portion of the joists firmly against the bottom chords. Every 8 feet a button is fastened up under the bottom chord by means of a 5/8" bolt which passes through a long joist. This helps to prevent swaying of the trusses.

ROOF

A complete roof truss was installed every 8 feet and secured by means of buttons as described above. The cross tie in these trusses had to be framed securely into the top chords to prevent any movement along the chords that might be caused by the lateral bracing. The secondary rafters, on their way from the ridge to the third chord, were also framed into the cross tie to work as knee bracing.

160

Raising roof truss by means of ginpole.
Photo by Glenn Baker

The thirty-one roof trusses had been fitted at our Ashland, New Hampshire shop, numbered and taken apart. When assembled in the bridge floor, these trusses were raised by a ginpole which was guyed to a V made of heavy timbers which were dragged forward each time a truss was placed. Upon reaching the end of the bridge floor, a 30' extension was built to accommodate the ginpole.

Arnold placing shingles on roof.

Photo by Glenn Baker

Arnold leveling a tempered steel falsework.
Photo by Glenn Baker

Placing last roof trusses from bridge floor extension.
Photo by Glenn Baker

The 3 foot shingles were nailed to 2 x 4 perlins. These perlins are 16" on center and the shingles are laid 16" to the weather. Having sat on one of the perlins on the roof for 8 weeks, Arnold finally nailed the last shingle onto the south side. The perlins and he had become moulded to produce the fit and comfort of an easy chair.

Showing cambre in trusses.   Photo by Glenn Baker

DORMERS

The covered bridge is one structure which can be modified in many ways, to match or be in harmony with its surroundings or to be physically sufficient in an abusive setting. In the case of the Zehnder's Holz-Brücke, it was desirable for the bridge to be strong for bus traffic and yet have the all-around feeling of mellowness and quaint touch of antiquity. It should be friendly to the Bavarian but not radical enough to offend its Yankee counterparts. When Tiny Zehnder casually dropped a word about dormers, I volunteered that I had yet to see a covered bridge with dormers. He may have anticipated a difference of opinion for in the next breath he said, "This is Frankenmuth". These dormers do add. They allow one to focus his attention on the bridge rather than on the immense roof. We built the six dormers in our shop and brought them as units to mount on the roof. They were set by the use of a ginpole and will be lighted.

Arnold preparing to lift dormer.

Photos by Glenn Baker

Arnold placing perlins and examining shingles.

East end shingled.

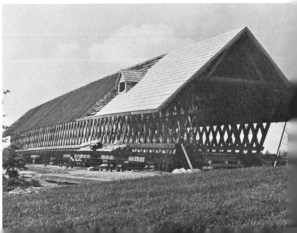

DOWN GRADE 20' TO THE FINAL LOCATION

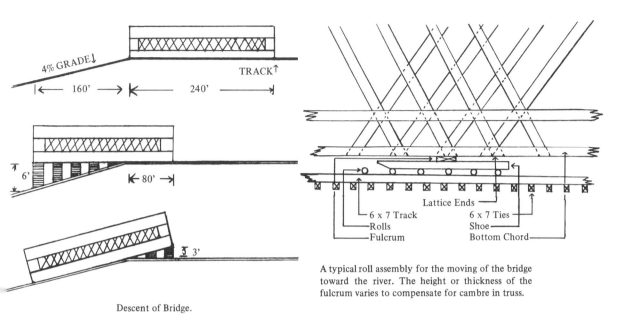

4% GRADE↓

TRACK↑

|← 160' →|← 240' →|

6'

|← 80' →|

3'

Descent of Bridge.

Lattice Ends
6 x 7 Track
Rolls
Fulcrum
6 x 7 Ties
Shoe
Bottom Chord

A typical roll assembly for the moving of the bridge toward the river. The height or thickness of the fulcrum varies to compensate for cambre in truss.

After the center 9 feet of the bridge floor was placed, the structure was ready to move. It was to be rolled about 500 feet in making a vertical descent of 20 feet. The west end of the bridge was at a point where the 4% grade met our level assembly area. We placed the bridge on 240' of level track with rolls at twenty locations.

Arthur Potter and Arnold compressing floor plank.   Photo by Glenn Baker

Arthur Potter drilling pilot holes in floor plank. Jeff Baker placing spikes. Arnold driving spikes.   Photo by Glenn Baker

One could coin a new term, "Bavarian Cooperation", after an experience in a strange town where contractors, church builders, insurance men, maintenance professionals, horse teamsters, ox teamsters, carpenters, commercial pilots, covered bridge buffs, printers, retired bookkeepers, and farmers came to offer their help in the bridge moving. There was need to increase our personnel from a total of 3 or 4 to 15. These good people helped us during the moving and in some cases for weeks

Capstan before oxen started moving forward.   Photo by Glenn Baker

before, with no thought of financial reward. They seemed to want to be a part of what they considered a "once-in-a-lifetime" town project.

At this time we had to excavate some 500 cubic yards of earth and place a 6" layer of crushed limestone to bring the grade to match the steel falsework at the west side of the river. It extended east with a 4% rise in grade to the break that was originally at the west end of the bridge. All that was left to do was to build our little double track railroad. We placed our 6" x 7" - 4' ties, 12" apart, in straight lines, and covered with a track of 4 or 5 lines of 6" x 7" timbers in 8 foot lengths.

The track was laid 200 feet down the grade. We then built an extension of the level track for a distance of 160 feet toward the river. This section of blocking between the now level track and the down grade track was 0' at the bridge end and 6' at the lower end. The bridge was then rolled forward 160'.

In this forward move we used the power of the oxen at the east end. With the price of Arabian oil going up each day, we decided it was more sensible, and economical to go "back to the farm". Surely Tiny Zehnder's herd of 250 head of prize cattle would not mind sharing a few bouquets of alfalfa with these cute little strangers!

When the oxen moved in, the board and room as agreed by Zehnders' was okay. Now, Mr. Hayhoe explained that his "boys" had been pampered and he could find no warm shower in the barn. He was right; there was none. Mr. Hayhoe was proud of his well-groomed oxen and promptly made arrangements for a march through the local car wash. Here each morning they were prepared for their public appearance by having a warm soap and water shower down from the "wading" line. The oxen were not disappointed in their accommodations!

Oxen off to their morning shower.   Photo by Glenn Baker

Aerial views of progress down the 4% grade.
Photos by Glenn Baker

The capstan was set up at the east end of the bridge. With the anchor at the east bridge abutment and the opposing force secured in the east end of the bridge floor, the oxen would give the appearance of pushing the bridge toward the river. After taking up the "slack" in the system, a forward movement of 3½" per revolution of the capstan could be assured.

As the bridge moved forward we had to straighten unruly rolls and move the loose ones around forward to enter again at each of the 20 stations.

One rainy day it was estimated that there were over 200 people under the bridge. None of them seemed to be afraid of the operation. It takes a bit of diplomacy to be able to tell all those folks how welcome they are and still try to work

168

in the very little remaining space. There rests the difference between the wooden covered bridge and the concrete monsters.

The point for our giant "teeter board" was established at the break in the grade and we proceeded to lower the west end of the bridge 6 feet while raising the east end 3 feet. During this operation we maintained the previously established tangent along the 240 feet of the bottom bridge roller shoes.

Having accomplished the changing of roller bearings from level to 4% grade, the next procedure was to build in blocking to hold the track from the grade-break east for 80 feet. This blocking was also to hold track from 0 to +3 feet from level. The rolling positions were all fitted with shims to a **precise** plane and then the jacks were removed.

At this time we had moved the capstan to the west side of the river, in the parking area. Though the bridge was nearly 400 feet from its final position the capstan would be only 30 feet from the west portal when the pull was complete. Oxen belonging to Mr. Alfred Hayhoe and Mr. Lloyd Maynard alternated in pulling as did two two-horse teams belonging to Mr. H. Reed and Mr. Sargent. Each time a team pulled the pole of the capstan around the circle, the bridge advanced 3½ inches.

To prevent the estimated 230 tons of now dry-land bridge from rolling out of control, we placed two snub-lines of 1¼" steel cable. These lines were secured to the understructure and extended for 150 feet to the rear, where they were attached to an eighteen ton bulldozer. When the "balance of power" between bulldozer and oxen became a smooth operation, a ten-wheel dump truck with a 12 cubic yard load of stone was substituted for the bulldozer by Mr. Lentner and his very accommodating "little" sons. They had use for the bulldozer elsewhere.

The resistance to forward movement in the bridge was maintained evenly by the heavy snub lines being held tightly enough to keep them a certain distance above the ground. This made a ready signal for more, or less, line restraint.

The oxen had a mechanical advantage of about 10 to 1 (disregarding friction) at the capstan. This was multiplied by 9 through a pair of quadruple blocks in the rope within the bridge, on the floor. When the rope crossing the river would become very straight, it was necessary at times to signal for a slight relaxing of steel cable at the other end of the bridge.

At first the progress was quite rapid. It was easy to work on the graded surface. We moved nearly 70' the

Henry Reed and his horses make the first pull forward.

Photo by Mr. Herzog

Arnold Graton, Milton Grāton, Tiny Zehnder, Bill Zehnder and John, the Pilot, entertain the Hayhoe oxen.

Photo by Glenn Baker

second day on this grade but soon reached the edge of the falsework where all placing ties, track and rolls had to be done from cat-walks. These walks also had to be built as we progressed. Material had to be carried along the cat-walks or handed down through the holes which were left open in the bridge floor. Much of the time the carrying distance reached 200'. About ten days were required to place the tracks for the first level move, and to move the 160'.

The plan had been made in early November to start down the grade on January 18th and to arrive in place spanning the river at 12 o'clock noon on January 29, 1980. I kept the tension on the 1½" rope during the entire pull. My accomplishment was producing an average of 75 pounds of tension on the line for a total of nearly a mile.

The oxen and horses were asked many times to yield their place to special interest groups ranging from a complete fifth grade class who walked all over me to the sedate Michigan Historical Commissioners who proved to be as careful as the oxen. Though a substantial net retaining force had to be maintained for safety, for short periods, it could be reduced to perhaps 4 or 5 tons. I had waited several days and anxiously for the arrival of members of Women's Lib who were reported to have threatened to take over my job, but no relief came.

On the final day of pulling, we were to arrive at noon! We placed oak blocks against the ccncrete abutment to maintain a 1" clearance, and then pulled until the bridge touched against these spacing blocks. It was a cold day and no one had a watch. The ribbon on the entrance to the north side was cut and 400 people swarmed onto that sidewalk. They proceeded across the end to the south walk and were half way back across the bridge when the noon whistle blew at The Star of West Flour Mill. We were at least 4 minutes early!

As Tiny Zehnder stepped off the bridge sidewalk he appeared happy and relieved. He said as he held out his hand to shake my rope-blistered one, "I am glad to see that the bridge reaches across the Cass River! Now, lets' have a Bavarian Chicken Dinner".

Tiny Zehnder and Milton Grāton.

Photo by Glenn Baker

THE LAST of the
COVERED BRIDGE BUILDERS

I wish to give credit to the following photographers and collectors for being allowed access to their collections:

Milton S. Grāton